# One Glorious Hour

*To*

*Brian Henton*

*With thanks to Louise Collins, Duncan Hamilton, Winifred Hawthorn, Stirling Moss, Tony Brooks, Nikki Lauda, James Hunt, Ronnie Peterson, Roy Salvadori, Brian Henton, David Purley, Innes Ireland, Rob Walker, Tim Parnell, Raymond Mays, Bill Boddy, Denis Jenkinson, Robin Herd, Chris Nixon, and Innes Lloyd, BBC TV producer and Tony Maylam, film director. Special thanks to Max Mosley and Bernie Ecclestone for inviting me into the world of Grand Prix.*

First published in Great Britain in 2012 by The Derby Books Publishing Company Limited, 3 The Parker Centre, Derby, DE21 4SZ.

© Don Shaw, 2012

ISBN 978-1-78091-043-7

Printed and bound by CPI Group (UK) Ltd, Croydon, CRO 4YY

# DON SHAW

# One Glorious Hour

*A man dies helping his best friend
who in return is called upon to
repay that debt by risking his own life.*

## THE MIKE HAWTHORN STORY

DB
PUBLISHING

*This is a 'lost' story, one that I discovered through my involvement in motor racing. It is a testament to the eternal values of friendship and self sacrifice in which guilt and redemption of that guilt is the central theme. It takes place in the highly dangerous arena of Grand Prix motor racing of the fifties, the bloodiest period in motor racing history. It was an age in which the drivers were still amateurs and the sport was untainted by the corruption of big money.*

# **Chapter** One

**Reims Grand Prix Circuit, 5 July 1958**

Mike Hawthorn, in a Ferrari Dino 246 racing car, dropped to a crawl on his return to the pits. He was driving slowly because he thought it dangerous to arrive back in pain. If it came to the attention of the stewards…

He automatically straightened his bow tie, a ritual he went through after every final practice, hoping it might bring him luck in the following day's race, the French Grand Prix. It was better doing it than not doing it, just in case. So far he had made his own luck, grabbing pole position on the grid with a best time of 2 minutes 21.7 seconds. He would remain on pole unless another driver beat that time in the last few minutes of the session. Normally he would have put in another flying lap trying to improve on his time, but decided against it because the pain, usually low grade, had become more acute.

Mike generally had his handicap under control. Off the track he would easily deal with a flare up by taking a Tylenol tablet (he found aspirin was not as effective as it had been in the past) and he would be fine and dandy, but he would never take them before competition. The art of cornering required rapid coordination of mind and body. Hitting the targeted braking point beforehand, then making fast gear changes on the racing line had to be repeated at each corner, lap after lap – that was how a world champion was made. He was afraid that his skills might be affected should Tylenol enter his system.

In his mirror he saw another Ferrari howling towards him and pulled over, punching the air eagerly in encouragement. His teammate Pete Collins, on his own flying lap, roared past without a gesture of acknowledgement, all his concentration needed for tackling the corner ahead.

In the Ferrari pits Louise Collins, Pete's wife, sat on a chair opposite the finish line, her pencil at the ready, tensely looking down the home straight for signs of her husband.

She hated the waiting, so when his car swung into view she visibly relaxed. For a moment the distant Ferrari seemed to hang above the hot tarmac like a shimmering red fly, but then it was real and hammering towards her. Eight seconds later she clicked the stopwatch clamped to her lap board and recorded that Pete had failed to beat his previous best time and would start the race in fourth place on the second row of the grid, behind Mike.

All four Ferrari drivers had now completed the practice session and Romolo Tavoni, the studious looking Italian team manager, would shortly be telephoning his 'Commendatore', Enzo Ferrari, with the good news that Mike had 'made pole'.

If Pete's failure to join Mike on the front row was a disappointment to Louise, it was a minor thing, far outweighed by the relief at his safe return. In any case she could never be jealous of Mike's achievement. After all, he was almost 'family'. When Louise married Pete, the handsome and charismatic racing driver from Kidderminster, he and Mike were already close friends, so close that they had been christened 'mon ami mates' after a cartoon running in the *Daily Express*.

Mike and Pete were amateurs. Their only income from Ferrari was a small annual retainer, plus the chance to win some prize money as a race winner. Commercial sponsorship, that latter day engine of wealth creation, was in its infancy – if not unborn. As 'best mates', in the truest sense of the term, each relied on the family garage businesses back home to maintain their mutual indulgence in fun, females and fast cars.

Motor racing for both of them, as it was with the majority of drivers, was the pursuit of thrills on the track and camaraderie off it. In this they were helped by Enzo Ferrari. To date Enzo had encouraged competition between his drivers, though no one knew what might happen should one of them take a substantial lead in the world championship table.

Viewed from outside the fan base, the view that the average man in the street had of racing drivers was fashioned in the aftermath of a world war. Mike's exploits on the track had made him something of a heroic figure for all ages, a flag carrier for a nation still suffering from post-war depression. The public relished anything that would lift the general gloom, add a bit of romance and excitement. Mike was keenly aware of this, knew that he was lucky. In coming from a garage business he always kept his respect for the 'salt of the earth' as he termed the skilled working man.

Apart from this he had no conscience about enjoying himself. He had been having a ball ever since he won his first event, the Brighton Speed Trials in

1950 when he had driven a Riley Sprite to victory in the quarter-mile dash along the sea front. There had followed exciting days, his parents and friends willing him on, the mandatory party afterwards, the booze, the girls. His joy had climaxed at Goodwood on Easter Monday 1952 when, displaying the blue bow tie that was to become iconic, he drove his privately entered Cooper-Bristol to win in great style, prompting the motor racing world to sit up and take notice. After the race he was the toast of the paddock and the party that followed embraced all the competitors, their families and friends.

Six months later Mike was overwhelmed when he was invited to join the celebrated Scuderia de Ferrari. The icing was on the cake, even if it drew some frowns from British aficionados who would have preferred Mike to have joined a British team, such as BRM or Vanwall.

In 1956 the boyishly handsome 'Pete' Collins joined him as the second English driver with Ferrari. He was the quieter of the two, with an easy charm that made him a magnet for women. The two men together, the tall Mike against the smaller Pete, became a regular twosome both in the paddock and on the prowl. They were like two schoolboys, up for any japes or tricks, and always with the eye for 'a bit of skirt'. Marriage was right out of the question for either of them – that is until Pete was struck dumb on meeting Louise. It was an instant recognition for them both, a meeting of kindred spirits. They were married within a week.

Louise King was famous in her own right as a leading American actress and star of *The Seven Year Itch* on Broadway. When she married Pete she had known him for only one week. Acutely sensitive, she felt that she had driven a wedge between the 'mon ami mates'. She was correct in her guesswork. Mike had been shocked that his close friendship with Pete had been broken within days. It pained him to think that Pete would no longer be available for a night on the town, the fun with the girls, the practical jokes.

When Pete told him he was marrying Louise Mike was highly peeved. 'What do you have to go and do that for, you stupid clot?' he said. 'Do you realise I'd have married you if you'd been a woman?' He then adopted Oliver Hardy's stoic look, with a slow deprecatory shake of the head, at which Pete became a mournful Stan Laurel. This prompted Mike to grab him by the throat and strangle him horribly, leaving Pete in a heap on the floor, gurgling and giggling.

Louise, with her sensitivity, detected Mike's disappointed reaction to Pete's marriage and quickly acted by inviting him to live with them between races on what was their second home, *Mipooka*, a boat moored in Monaco harbour and mostly funded by Louise's father. It was not a difficult move as she liked Mike for his talent in making her laugh.

To the public at large she had already demonstrated her good and unselfish nature by sending a congratulatory cable to Marilyn Monroe for beating her to the star role in a movie version of *The Seven Year Itch*.

Soon the trio became a familiar sight at European races, either in the hotel, circuit paddock or when walking down the pit lane. They would often be seen laughing at some crack from Mike or an ironic comment from Pete. Louise wrote to her parents that she was supremely happy, surely one of the 'three luckiest people in the world'.

On 2 July Pete and Louise were having breakfast on deck when Mike came up from his cabin.

'Coffee's in the galley keeping hot Mike,' said Louise, spotting him.

'Thanks. I've got to nip up to American Express. Expecting a telegram.'

They watched him step on shore. Louise thought he looked a little paler than usual.

On his return 20 minutes later he told them that he had a problem with his family business, the TT Garage in Farnham, and would have to get back there for a couple of days. His eyes had flickered at Louise as he said it, giving her food for thought after he had departed.

'I didn't think Mike looked too well Pete,' she said. 'Do you think there's something wrong?'

Pete was less worried. 'No, he gets stomach upsets. When he was in the Monza race last week his insides got shook up. Nothing to worry about.'

'Good. I'm glad.' Louise forgot her concern for Mike. Were they not the luckiest people in the world?

Pete was correct in telling Louise that Mike had been 'shook up' during the event that had taken place on Sunday 29 June the previous week. The 'Monza 500' mile trophy race was always a feat of endurance for any driver, but for Mike especially. His susceptibility to internal damage had to be kept a secret, even from those closest to him, lest it threaten his chances of winning the world championship. It was in pursuit of a solution to this problem that had sent him urgently to London.

\* \* \* \* \*

On the way back to the pits Mike came across a bunch of cheering British fans lining the tarmac, but then was forced to veer wide when one of them stepped out waving a Union Jack. Track invasion was not that unusual at a time when the sum total of safety precautions at race circuits amounted to no more than a sign warning spectators that 'motor racing is dangerous'.

During the Argentine Grand Prix in 1953, Mike's first race with Ferrari, 19 spectators had died, nine of them killed by waving their jackets at oncoming drivers like matadors taunting the bull.

But safety was never an issue. Racing cars were not even equipped with seat belts, the drivers preferring to be thrown out rather than struggle to escape an inferno that could quickly engulf a car, especially one built from aluminium like the Ferrari. Fireproof clothing was unheard of. In the wide open cockpit Mike's vulnerability was evident in his race attire: white trousers, a white shirt, a white spotted blue bow tie and a green gabardine jacket, the sort of clobber that might be seen on a bowling green.

It was this exposure to risk that gave racing drivers their cult status, similar to that of fighter pilots for they, too, compensated for the dangers they ran by playing hard, indulging in practical jokes and chasing women.

And it was no coincidence that it was the fighter pilot's slang that the motor racing fraternity adopted. Thus a driver did not 'die' in an accident. He either 'bought it', or 'got the chop' in a 'shunt'.

As Mike proceeded gently around the back of the circuit, another British fan stepped out, not waving a flag this time but instead offering Mike a glass of beer. He was one of a bunch of young engineering students, Mike's peer group when he was younger.

He still wore their 'uniform' of the ubiquitous Harris tweed or sports jacket, university tie, ratting cap, corduroy trousers and Veldtschoen shoes on some social occasions.

Mike, disposed towards them as he was, declined the offer with a grin and shake of the head. It brought a deep bow from the fan who withdrew, quaffing his beer to laughter and applause.

If only they knew…

It was a cruel irony, he reflected, that they envied him while he envied them. He envied their optimism that the world, despite the perils of the Cold War between East and West, was going to be a much better, wealthier and happier place.

'Fuck it.'

He spat out the expletive.

The fun of living the life of a racing driver had begun to pale after his first visit to Guy's Hospital, London, in late 1953 and then again in the spring of 1954. On his second visit, the Urology consultant had put to him a question: 'Why do you keep doing the very thing I warned you about a year ago? Motor racing's not the thing you should be doing with that kidney.'

It was while he was on board *Mipooka*, and supposedly getting ready to leave for the French Grand Prix at Reims, that he had been hit by a sharper pain than usual. It was this that had sent him to the American Express office that morning. Somehow he had to see his consultant, fearing that the 500 mile race at Monza, something that Enzo had forced him to take part in, had done real damage, the kind that the consultant had warned him about five years earlier: 'Mike. Newton's First Law. The driver in the car travels at the same speed as the car. You're barrelling down the straight at 170 miles an hour, or whatever. When you do hit the brakes your kidneys don't stop. Although…'

'Yeh, okay. I know.' Mike cut in, giving a dismissive flap of the hand. He had an engineering background and understood. Then he realised he had made a mistake as the consultant stared at him. 'Sorry, I know what you mean, the kidneys brake, they get pressured.'

'Yes. After the longitudinal g-force at the end of a straight what happens next?'

'I corner. I swap longitudinal g-force for lateral g-force.' Mike hated being treated like a schoolboy.

His flash of pique irritated the consultant. 'I'll make it technical then. The kidneys are protected by muscles but we don't know the effect of high g on them. We also don't know what effect vibration on the resonance frequency of internal organs has, especially any that are diseased.

'Heavy deceleration over long periods speeds up the aging process. Tissues break down, capillaries break down. I worked out there are, on average, 13 corners at a race track, about 60 laps in a Grand Prix. It adds up to about sixteen hundred extreme g-forces per race.'

Mike was silenced and nodded in acceptance and apology.

'Sorry, I didn't mean…'

In the summer of 1958, after his sudden departure from *Mipooka* to 'sort out a problem with his TT Garage' he had arrived at Guy's Hospital to find out that his left kidney had failed. Had it been precipitated by hurtling round the steeply banked sections of the Monza track?

Mike told the consultant that he had done his best, had tried to get out of the race but Enzo Ferrari had insisted that he took part. Unable to disclose his illness, Mike had no alternative but to obey.

'Why don't you quit racing?' Your health is more important than anything isn't it?'

The consultant's direct question threw him a little. He hesitated, caught his breath in an attempt to explain, but gave up. His answer would have sounded silly and stupid, not something that could be expressed in words. Quite simply he wanted to stand on the winner's rostrum at the end of the Grand Prix season with the world champion's wreath of laurels around his neck. In that moment of becoming the first British world motor racing champion he would live a lifetime.

'One crowded hour of glorious life
is worth an age without a name'

Mike did not read poetry. He had never heard of the poet, Mordaunt. They were simply two lines that he had seen on a headstone while attending the funeral of a fellow racing driver. He remembered them because they had seemed appropriate to his situation.

It was not just the pursuit of the world championship that kept him going. Each race leading up to it provided the 'crowded hour' – or two – in which the thrill of the adrenalin rush masked any physical pain. Nowhere else and in no other time was he so intensely alive.

No, nothing would stop him now, not with only six races to go. And he had the mental toughness to see it through. He had proved it to himself, time and time again, hadn't he?

Okay, it had been a tough ride these last five years but he had gradually built up a defence mechanism based on common sense plus logic. He talked to himself on the way home:

'Of course the doc tells me to stop. It's to cover himself. But the fact is there's only six races left. The kidney's gone through 54 already – Grand Prix and others. It worked for five years of racing before it packed up. The other's bound to last just six more and survive. Come on, for fuck's sake!'

He gave himself a big fat reassuring grin, the famous one, the one that featured on both the front and back pages of the dailies. It was a trick that actually worked. He did indeed feel better when he grinned. So he dared get tougher with himself, playing devil's advocate.

'Okay, you stupid clot. You might die. Think of it. Bloody dead. At 28! Are you insane?'

He dealt with it in cavalier fashion. 'Look. It's a risk every time I go on the track. The death rate on a race track is one every…'

'Jesus. Stop it.'

Mike got home and telephoned the team hotel in Reims. Pete had just arrived and took the call. To save money his message was brief, 'Mate, keep the fizz on ice.'

He did need to save money – and it had nothing to do with his garage business. It was all about the welfare and upkeep of a mother and son who lived in France, another close secret that he kept. Then there was the problem of his own mother, Winifred. In 1954 her husband, Leslie, had died in a road accident leaving his garage business to be managed by Mike. But with him frequently abroad Winifred had to step in and help. What would become of her in old age, she had wanted to know, should he die on the race track as had so many of his contemporaries?

As he cruised slowly around the back of the circuit he knew that, whatever the outcome, he had given himself one last shot at becoming world champion. If he achieved that goal it would certainly ring up the garage cash till, pulling in customers from far and wide only too happy to buy cars from the 'Golden Boy' as he was known to the readers of the popular press. And there would be extra income from opening technical colleges and businesses, giving after dinner speeches – and think of the 'skirt' he could pull.

Then, when he had supped his fill of the boisterous and lustful life, he just might get married and have a family.

'Fuck it.' This time the expletive was spat out because of the pain. He was worried that he might get back to the pits before it had gone. A doctor might be called and his secret discovered. That would not do at all. Grimly, he took another Tylenol.

Mike's finances and illness had not been his only problems. The fun that he had innocently sought through motor racing had been marred by other events. First, there had been the furore created over his apparent avoidance of serving two years of compulsory National Service in the armed forces. It was assumed that he used his international travel as an excuse. Even the consultant, who had a copy of the day's edition of the *Daily Mirror* to hand, had referred to it on his first visit to the hospital in 1953. 'Let me read you some of the leader column,' he said, picking up the newspaper.

'Here is a big-headed young man who thumbs his nose at his country. He prefers to stay abroad driving Italian racing cars. He does not intend to do his National Service. Nab him the next time he returns. Has Mr Hawthorn anything to say in his defence? If so we'll gladly print it.'

The consultant had raised his eyebrows. 'Well? Why don't you? Speak in your defence? Tell everybody you failed your army medical. You've got half the nation complaining about you. It's a wonder you've got any fans left.'

Mike had already received abusive letters from army conscripts, angry that he was allowed to gallivant around the world while they were forced to wear a uniform for two years. This had resulted in a drop in his fan base leaving him helpless, unable to tell the world that he had failed his army medical due to a kidney problem.

'Oh yes,' he had told the consultant. 'I can prove I'm not a cheat and I'll get loads more fans. Great. Fans of a banned racing driver because he's got a dodgy kidney. They'll take away my racing licence!'

'So what are you going to do?'

'I want to be world champion. And afterwards you can write me a letter saying what was wrong with me. I'll go public with it, prove I wasn't a cheat.'

'That's what you want as your epitaph, is it?' The consultant was open and frank. 'A world champion. He was not a cheat?'

Mike's confidante, Duncan Hamilton, a Jaguar car dealer and occasional racing driver, had preceded Pete Collins as his best mate and was resolved that he would try to do everything he could to help his friend in need. He listened to Winifred pour out her anxiety that Mike might die either in an accident, or from his illness. He continued to counsel her over the years as Mike carried on racing interspersed with hospital checks. After each visit the medical notes ominously referred to the left kidney as 'continuing to swell'.

By the time of the 1958 Grand Prix at Reims the press had forgotten Mike's failure to do his National Service, as had most of his fans. But there was another part of Mike's emotional baggage that was far more disturbing. It had arisen from a race accident, the effects of which had him screaming in the middle of the night. It was a result of the greatest tragedy in motor racing – and still remains to this day – one that was so appalling that it nearly led to the demise of motor racing as a sport. Even the Pope had pronounced it to be a 'work of evil'.

It had the overall effect of turning Duncan from being a sympathetic listener to Winifred's outpourings into a counsellor supreme – but not for her, for Mike.

The accident occurred in 1955 when Duncan joined Mike as a Jaguar driver in the 24 Hours Race at Le Mans, having won the race himself the previous year.

In his Jaguar D-Type Mike had braked to pull into a set of pits that occupied nothing more than a widened stretch of race track. His manoeuvre had forced the Austin Healey driver on his tail to swerve towards the centre of the track. This had led to a Mercedes hitting its rear end catapulting it into the crowd. Eighty-four spectators had died, a number of them decapitated. There were over 100 injured.

Mike saw the carnage and had stumbled around the paddock in hysteria.

The official enquiry had exonerated him, calling it a 'racing accident', but he could not escape the torment of knowing that it was his actions that had caused the tragedy. Initially determined never to get behind the wheel of another racing car, he was finally persuaded by Duncan to accept that it was the Le Mans circuit owners who were responsible for the accident by not providing pits that were separated from the track.

Even so, the ensuing nightmares and post traumatic shocks would have defeated him, had he lacked the will to become the first British driver to win the World Drivers' Championship. Duncan had suggested to him that his determination to achieve that goal was strengthened by his inner need to defeat his demons. It was a cunning little suggestion, but it worked. Mike was indeed given added strength. For, if there was any chance of eradicating his nightmares by focusing on becoming the first British World Drivers' Champion then he would try hard, 'bloody hard'. He refused to fold up, not now, not after what he had been through. It was something even to die for...

* * * * *

But, as Mike toured slowly back to the pits and still in pain, he knew that it was one thing to summon up the required confidence and commitment and another to achieve his goal since there were other drivers as eager as he was to win that coveted title.

The favourite for the world title was another Englishman, but not Peter Collins.

Currently that driver topped the world championship table, admittedly by a narrow margin from Mike. As he continued his slow journey back to the pits Mike glanced sideways as a Vanwall car drew up alongside, its driver the physical manifestation of that threat. Stirling Moss, wearing a white helmet, grinned at Mike whose response was to give him a vulgar two-fingered gesture. Stirling grinned even more, gave him two fingers in return and pulled away.

Mike grimaced. Stirling reminded him that he might be damaging himself in the pursuit of something that he might never achieve. The world championship was not something he could win entirely by his own efforts. If anything, the championship was in Stirling's gift, as he was arguably the better driver. Mike was also at a disadvantage as the dentist's son from London had an amazing charisma, his supreme self confidence evident in the way he talked and moved. Stirling by name, stirling by nature. A fighter, a winner. Smaller and slimmer, serious minded and focused, Stirling looked more the part of a racing driver than did Mike. He certainly performed like one. He was so good a driver that he was likely to grab maximum points in any race, providing his car was on the track and not in the garage under repair. Not only that, Stirling was popular with the fans for choosing to drive British cars. Unfortunately for him the Vanwall was not in the Ferrari class of reliability. His fans, realising that he sacrificed championship points by his choice were even more supportive when, just before leaving for France, he declared that it was 'Better to lose honourably in a British car than win in a foreign one'.

Mike could not claim to have that degree of patriotism since Ferrari had contracted him early in his career and a winning team was hard to abandon.

There was one thing, however, that stood in his favour in comparison with Stirling. He could take comfort in the fact that Stirling fell short of outright public acclamation by announcing that it was his ambition to become a professional racing driver, the first of his kind in Britain. The fans, still wedded to the notion that amateurism in British sport was a virtue, scorned the idea of professional sport generally.

This difference between the two men was most marked at the Monza 500 race, the one that Mike had dreaded. Before the race Stirling had posed for photographs in front of a Maserati racing car that bore the advertising decal, 'El Dorado Ice Cream'.

This was the first time advertising had moved from the occasional slogan on a trackside banner onto a racing car. The press photographers seized on it and had Mike staring at the monstrosity in mock horror. Okay, the message went out, let Stirling become professional but he, the Golden Boy, would remain the honourable amateur.

Mike was not an amateur by choice, but by education. He was still firmly rooted in an age when 'Gentlemen' cricketers (amateurs) still played against the 'Players' (professionals) in the annual match held at Lords. And in tennis it was often an amateur who won the Wimbledon Open. The British had given the world a number of sports, including rugby. It hardly mattered who won or lost. It was all a matter of 'playing the game', as valid in 1958 as much as it had been in the hey day of C.B. Fry. Amateurism in motor racing – individuals coming together to test their machines and skill – was how the sport had begun and its ethos still held after the Second World War. It did not mean that they were less serious – than was the budding professional, Stirling – in competing against each other. In seeking to win a race they were as competitive as he, though in the matter of training and application Stirling remained unbeaten. Not for him the japes and hoaxes before a race, the drinking and the womanising.

Stirling marked his 'professionalism' by retiring to his hotel bedroom earlier than the rest, the attention paid to his physical health being markedly different from that shown by Mike, whose love of carousing or womanising until the early hours was now almost legendary.

\* \* \* \* \*

He watched the tail of Stirling's car swing out of sight at the next turn then closed his eyes momentarily. Thank God, the pain was going.

Maybe, just maybe, the right kidney had not suffered too greatly at Monza. He hurriedly tried to think about more pressing matters to help dismiss his lingering depression. First, he tried to concentrate on the handling and performance of his car in order to give some sort of feedback for Tavoni. He now felt certain that it was the mixing of drum and disc brakes that had caused the persistent, though mild understeer, whereas Tavoni believed it was the design of the light and rigid chassis that was the cause. But then he dismissed the thought. His V6 2.4 litre engine of 280 horse power pulling 8,800 revolutions had behaved as well as could be expected.

'You're on pole', he told himself. That, in itself, spoke volumes for the car's handling. He would tell Tavoni that he had no trouble with understeer. As far as he was concerned the car was set up and ready to race.

He now turned his mind to weigh up the opposition other than Stirling. There was the great Juan Manuel Fangio taking part in his last Grand Prix and keen to retire with a win. And there were other talented and equally determined competitors ready to attack at the slightest opportunity, not least Luigi Musso and the fourth Ferrari driver, 'Taffy' Von Trips. Then came Jack Brabham, Phil Hill, Tony Brooks, Jo Bonnier, Roy Salvadori, Jean Behra, Graham Hill and Maurice Trintignant, all of them seasoned campaigners.

And there would be Pete Collins.

The thought of his mon ami mate brought a grimace. Pete was, if anything, too good a friend. He had told Mike, as they sat down for breakfast on the eve of final practice, that if he found he was losing too many points and unable himself to mount a serious challenge for the world championship, then he would help Mike to claim the crown.

Mike had taken a furtive glance at Pete. Did he *know*? He covered his uncertainty by telling Pete that he would have none of it, that he wanted to win on his own terms. It sounded pretentious and Pete had laughed outright. It had brought a silly grin from Mike who had then proceeded to throttle him.

But did Pete know? The thought had been troubling Mike ever since he had left *Mipooka* bound for Guy's hospital. But surely, he told himself, had Pete known of his illness it was a pound to a penny he would have been unable to stop himself from being a pest, getting himself all stupid and emotional. And it was another easy bet that he would have confided in Louise. And God knows where that would have led.

He tried to forget that particular worry, promising himself that he would keep the secret safe between himself and Duncan, that he would not jeopardise his mission. He had already decided there was no going back, had he not? Why torture himself? Leave it at that. His simple strategy for remaining race fit – he had told Duncan the previous night as they stood at the brass rail around the bar of the Grand Hotel Du Nord – was to miss all of the remaining non-Grand Prix races.

'I'm not letting Enzo force me out on any more banked tracks like Monza. I know I've got to go there for the Italian, but for any others I'll have the flu, or a bad back. Enzo won't sack me if he thinks I've any chance of the world championship. Here's to winning the French.'

Mike, clinked glasses with Duncan. The burly, jovial man grinned and held back his fears.

Mike knew he had them.

*  *  *  *  *

Thank God, the pain had gone.

He motored towards the pits, opposite the Shell Grandstand, a long low wooden structure with hand-painted advertisements in red and blue along the length of its pelmit. Behind it lay the paddock in which stood the transporters and the odd motor home. The usual rest place for a racing driver was a domestic caravan, given the lack of money in the sport. He stopped the car by the pit counter and clambered out to be met by Tavoni.

'Mike. On pole. Magnifico. Okay? Still got understeer?' Tavoni, a tall and dignified man, adjusted his spectacles.

'Yeh, a bit. But no problem.' Mike pulled off his blue helmet with its attached visor.

'I dropped the hammer out of the right hander.' He gestured towards the first corner of the circuit a kilometre ahead. 'I took it flat out, came out pulling eight-eight.'

Tavoni made a note on a card in his hand. 'We're doing well,' he said dryly. 'Everybody still runs on whisky. We run on gas.'

Mike laughed politely at Tavoni's joke. Ferrari had been helped that season by switching early from an alcohol based fuel to using top grade commercial petrol. Adjustments to their engines before the start of the season meant that Ferrari had an advantage over other teams slow in reacting to the change in the law.

A guffaw in Mike's ear, accompanied by a slap on his back, announced the arrival of Harry Schell. He was American and had been a tank commander in World War Two.

'Great Mike. Terrific.'

'Thanks Harry.' Mike grinned and put an arm around Harry's shoulder. 'How did you do?'

'I'm on the front row with you, you old fuck!'

Mike laughed. 'In that bloody BRM!' Mike referred to the British car that Stirling had driven in Grand Prix races in a previous year. Stirling liked it because it was British. Mike, when he heard of it, wished that he could have said the same.

He then spotted Luigi Musso pulling up in his Ferrari, an Italian who had a very real chance of winning the championship. Mike went to congratulate him for winning second place on the starting grid.

Luigi, dark and handsome and who normally wore a big smile if he had performed well, merely nodded, his eyes downcast. But as he climbed out of the car he stopped to stare at Mike, his lower lip trembling, the light of desperation in his eyes. He drew in a breath, was about to let it all burst forth when Mike was distracted by Duncan coming up to poke him in the stomach.

'You brilliant bugger.' Duncan put an arm round his shoulders and guided him into the paddock for a welcome mug of tea in the motor home.

As he added milk he hesitated. 'Notice anything about Luigi?'

Mike looked at him. 'Yeah. I did. Just now. What's up with him?'

'I saw him get a telegram. He read it and I'm buggered if he didn't turn white.'

'He'd been on the job all night,' Mike said dryly and laughed. Luigi had a very passionate lover who insisted on accompanying him at every race meeting.

Or was he still upset over his treatment by the team? It was generally known that he was dissatisfied with the way – as he perceived it – his car was dealt with by the mechanics, compared with that lavished on the cars of the two Englishmen. Or was it just Pete, in particular, of whom he was jealous? There was some basis for his complaint in that Enzo Ferrari often invited Pete for a meal whenever he was at Maranello, the team headquarters. Mike hardly minded. Pete could speak Italian and he could not. It was as simple as that as far as he was concerned.

Mind, he did feel a tad sorry for Luigi in that he was the only Italian driver with Ferrari and so bore the expectations of the millions of Italians who loved the *machina*, having a passion for motor racing that was reflected by the blood red colour of the Ferrari racing car itself. It was fervently hoped that it would be Luigi who would drive a Ferrari to victory, not Mike Hawthorn. After all, the Englishman only led him in the world championship table by a mere four points. Thus, on the eve of the French Grand Prix of 1958, of the four man Scuderia de Ferrari team, the huge pressure on Luigi was undeniable.

But what had made him turn pale? Why the downright fear?

Mike drank his tea and dismissed his thoughts about Luigi. He had enough of his own troubles, more than enough, to worry about an Italian with whom he could not even converse.

* * * * *

On the journey back to the hotel there were five friends crammed into the Renault Floride drophead, its colour British racing green. In Mike's first race with Ferrari the Commendatore had his car painted exactly that same colour, an honour that he never bestowed again on any other foreign driver, whatever their nationality. It was something that Mike never forgot and had thanked the great man accordingly. Later, he discovered that he rarely did anything out of the goodness of his heart that did not benefit himself or the Scuderia in some way.

Louise and Pete sat in the rear of the car, Mike stuck between them, wearing his familiar ratting cap and with a pipe clenched between his teeth. The driver was Von Trips, the fourth Ferrari driver who was not having the best of seasons. Duncan sat in the front passenger seat.

Louise started to sing the Sinatra hit number of 1958, *All the Way* then broke off as the men let out a cheer. Stirling Moss had drawn alongside in an Austin Healey sports car driven by his fellow Vanwall teammate Stuart Lewis-Evans, the small and lightly built driver from Bedfordshire. Stirling, as usual, was giving them the two fingers.

Mike returned the salute and shouted out the slogan found on the Walls ice cream boxed tricycles, 'Stop Me And Buy One!' Then he added 'El Dorado!'

At this Stirling gave him more 'two fingers'. It had Mike roaring with laughter. Stuart sped away laughing, with Stirling still grinning and gesturing.

The fun continued in the hotel, initially without Mike's involvement. Now, with another Tylenol inside him, he was on the prowl intent on seeking out the girl whom he had seen at the track perched on a neighbouring pit counter and giving him the eye.

He found her by chance in the lobby. She smiled at his grin, opened her mouth slightly and put the tip of her tongue on the edge of her teeth.

Later, having smuggled her into his room, Mike paused in the doorway as he caught sight of Stuart Lewis-Evans falling victim to a plastic jar of water perched over his bedroom door. It was followed by a huge belly laugh from Harry Schell, the perpetrator.

And then Mike watched Stuart get his revenge on Harry with itching powder bought from Alf's Joke Shop back home in Luton.

Mike felt he had to join in, despite the girl waiting in his room. It developed into the kind of alcohol fuelled rowdiness that always ends in something dramatic – and so it proved with Mike dumping a bucket of water over Stuart's head. It was only then that he went back to the bedroom to placate the girl.

Stuart and Harry waited until Mike was in bed and then, suppressing their giggles, pulled a fire hose the length of the corridor, stopping outside Mike's bedroom.

With a pass key 'borrowed' from hotel reception, they carefully unlocked the door and leapt in, aiming the hose and letting fly. The girl's screams and Mike's shout woke up Stirling in the next room, at which he sighed, turned over and tried to get back to sleep.

The next morning the hotel manager, a man who had fought with the French Resistance against the Nazi occupation, was delighted to receive a cheque in payment for the damage caused and waved the party away in gratitude.

They left the hotel at 9.40am, the route taking them south-west from the centre of town to pick up the D27 for the village of Thillois. From there it was a short journey to the circuit paddock. It promised to be a fine day and not too warm, ideal for the race.

Mike, Pete, Louise and Duncan once more shared the Floride open top tourer but this time Luigi Musso had joined them as Taffy had left earlier with *The Observer* sports writer, Peter Lewis. Mike observed that Luigi's eyes showed dark smudges beneath.

Louise was nervous as they set off, trying not to think about the race and so talked to Pete about *Mipooka* needing a good clean and should they use the main charter company or the other, smaller firm – and when was the boat's next service due?

Stuart and Stirling were the last to leave the hotel in their Austin Healey. This time Stirling drove, overtaking the Floride at speed. If he was laying down a marker for the race, Mike ignored it. He had to maintain his energy flow and calm concentration. Just of late he had begun to feel a little tired during the day and sometimes needed to rest. He was determined to enjoy the day. That meant winning the race.

But he bargained without considering the Malevolent Fates.

# Chapter Two

**Reims, 6 July**

Louise Collins was not the only actress in the Ferrari pits before the start of the French Grand Prix. Carlotta Mancini, who had acted in one or two romantic movies, was as sexy looking as any of the drivers' girlfriends or wives who, in time honoured tradition, decorated the pits at race meetings. It is doubtful, though, that any ever felt as she did right now. Yes, nervous and apprehensive prior to the race, but certainly not hating.

She stood in a corner of the garage watching her lover, Luigi Musso, humiliate himself as he pleaded with Tavoni. She heard him use the expression, *mafiosi*. His story had such impact that the most inscrutable of team managers recoiled, paused and then bent to speak urgently, but quietly, into Luigi's ear. He made it clear that there was nothing he could do to help. Even if he tried to 'arrange' that Luigi won the winner's prize money – which he would never do – it was far, far too late for that. He advised Luigi to go to the police with his story after the race, whether he won or lost.

Luigi's problems had started earlier in the season when Carlotta told him that she had seen Peter Collins with Enzo Ferrari and that he had worked his way into Enzo's affections by dubious means. There was even talk, she claimed, of the two Englishmen receiving a much higher retainer from Enzo than that which he enjoyed. She urged him to claim what was rightfully his. Did he not deserve a share in *la dolce vita* as he took the same risks as they did? Carlotta was vindicated when she overheard a conversation between two of the Ferrari mechanics and related it to Luigi.

'Collins and Hawthorn have an agreement,' she told him. 'Whichever of them wins a race they share the prize money equally. Strength comes in numbers and they are united against you. Enzo is obviously backing it or else he'd stop it, wouldn't he?'

It was not difficult to fuel Luigi's anger. He could ill afford the maintenance of his separated family, his wife and two children whom he had left for Carlotta in 1952. Driven by his need to make some 'real' money and encouraged by his lover he went into partnership with a businessman aimed at importing Pontiac Bonneville cars, manufactured in the USA. From the beginning the arrangement had been dogged with all manner of problems, not to mention the lack of consumer interest in Italy, a country that was fiercely loyal to its own car manufacturers. The company had gone bankrupt and now the 'businessman' was making threats should Luigi fail to return his investment. It was then that Luigi, to his horror, found out that his so-called partner had friends in the Neapolitan Comorra, that branch of the mafia that was notorious for its ruthlessness.

Just before they left the hotel on the morning of race day Luigi had taken a telephone call from his 'partner'. It carried more than the vague threat that had been conveyed in the telegram of the previous day and which had aroused the concern of Duncan. He had ordered Luigi to win the race and hand over the prize money by 8pm that same evening. Luigi had pleaded with him, unsuccessfully, that he was not a favourite to win. It was odds on that the victor would be either Mike Hawthorn, Pete Collins or Stirling Moss. At this point the partner had interrupted him, making it clear that Luigi would suffer if the money was not paid on time. Luigi showed his terror in his outlandish pleading to Tavoni to do something, anything, that would ensure he won the race.

But all that Tavoni could do was assure him that his car was set up for racing to the same standard as that of Hawthorn and Collins. His final words were, 'Go out and win'. He squeezed Luigi's arm and turned away to attend to the remainder of his pre-race check list. But his hard breathing betrayed his lingering shock.

Luigi was left stranded, looking at Carlotta in a slough of shame and misery. In return she knitted her eyebrows in dreadful pity, her eyes filling with tears.

A sudden burst of amusement from outside the garage brought Carlotta's head round in the direction from which it had come, tightening her lips. She saw the *uomini anglais*, Hawthorn and Collins, with their heads back, rocking with laughter. She disliked Hawthorn in particular as he was a constant lecher. Luigi had told her that during the Monaco Grand Prix Hawthorn's car had broken down outside a house. There, standing in a window, had been a girl asking if he would like a glass of water. He had stayed in the house until the race was over, having drunk 'several glasses of water' and had been seen emerging with a self-satisfied smile on his face, much refreshed. And had he not boasted about his easy lay?

In her eyes Collins and Hawthorn were nothing more than rich playboys compared with Luigi who had to work hard for a basic living in what was one of the most dangerous occupations on earth. Not for him the luxury of an *affascinante* yacht moored in Monaco or a motor business back home. Carlotta, though prudish in many ways, did not regard herself as immoral in having fallen in love with a married man. She would marry him instantly if it were possible, but, of course, it was not, divorce being forbidden by the Church of Rome and illegal under law.

Luigi had told her of a French girl, Jacqueline Delaunay, who had been seduced by Hawthorn at the time of the French Grand Prix in 1953 and subsequently given birth to his son. When she found out that she was pregnant her father had been outraged.

It was a scandalous affair that had taken place in the heart of a deeply Catholic community where contraception and abortion were also illegal, not to say immoral. This was the sum total of Luigi's knowledge of the matter. Carlotta seized on it as another example of Hawthorn's immorality.

Both remained ignorant of the rest of the story. When her son was born Jacqueline had been thrown out of the family home and given a small place to live in the back streets of Reims. She had appealed to Mike for financial help. He had asked for proof since having had casual sex with him might point to her being promiscuous. He agreed to meet her at the 1956 French Grand Prix when he would be introduced to the child. Mike recognised himself immediately in the fair haired little boy with the square jaw and dazzling smile and embraced him. Jacqueline had named him Arnaud Michael, but insisted that everybody called him Mike. 'Father Mike' then promised Jacqueline that he would look after them both financially until the boy grew up.

At the French Grand Prix in 1957 he had asked Tavoni to ensure that all of his prize money, if any, should be handed to him in cash immediately, rather than come to him in the form of a cheque at a later date. When asked why he wanted the money so urgently he replied 'For humanitarian reasons' and said it with an expression that brooked no argument. It was the same now in 1958. He only had one charity and that was Jacqueline and Arnaud Michael. He was aware that, as the boy grew older, his upkeep would become much more expensive, nevertheless he had made his promise and would hold himself to that commitment.

Carlotta knew none of this. She also overlooked, deliberately or otherwise, the fact that Enzo was looking for a new world champion with whom to promote his business. He saw clearly that Mike as a racing driver looked more like a putative world champion than any other driver in the team. And, as a bonus, he instinctively liked Mike, liked his flair and flamboyance.

Collins was a different matter, in that his offence was to curry favour with Enzo Ferrari at the expense of her Luigi. Oh, but it was true! Had not Luigi told her time and time again of how Collins had wormed his way into Enzo's affections?

She would challenge friends – and anyone who would listen – that as long as he treated Collins as a surrogate son after the death of his real son, Dino, was he not bound to instruct Tavoni to give special attention to his race car? And was this not bound to demoralise Luigi who was a true Italian *patriota*, the pride of all Italy? And was it not obvious that Hawthorn's car had also been given special treatment in that Enzo was on record as backing him to win the world championship above all the rest? To sum up, were not both Englishmen being given preferential attention to Luigi's disadvantage?

'Si o no?' she demanded.

Carlotta's grasp of the Collins-Enzo relationship was correct but she had no idea of the situation that had led up to it. It was true that Enzo had adopted Pete Collins as his surrogate son following the death of his real son, Dino, in 1956 from muscular dystrophy. But, if she had probed deeper, she would have learnt that Collins had won that affection through his care and devotion to Dino over the long months of his dying year. While Dino was confined to his room Pete had visited him as often as possible and had spent time asking about his student days at Bologna University, or the years he had spent in Switzerland studying for his engineering degree. Sometimes Pete brought with him one of his three dimensional puzzles for them to solve or maybe a kit for making a model boat on which they could work together.

Alternatively, they might eat fruit and lounge around discussing the latest lay out for Ferrari's new 1.5 litre Formula 2 engine. Once Pete had Dino laughing by telling him a story about the love life of the most handsome of the factory engineers.

Carlotta was not only wrong in her assessment of Mike and Pete but also in her opinion of Enzo himself. The Commendatore had been genuinely amazed at the time devoted by Pete to his dying son. He had even spent many hours in cinemas watching films that Dino would have loved to have seen but could not, being confined to his sick bed. Pete, whose memory was extraordinary, would return and describe each film in detail, even acting out some of the parts. *Wages of Fear* was a French film of such suspense that Dino had listened to the story line with baited breath all the way to its explosive climax.

At the end of 'watching' his last film by proxy, Hitchcock's *Vertigo*, he had lain back on his bed, sincerely grateful. 'Pete, I am like a small bird in a big cage. You set me free. You bring me the world. Grazie my friend for everything. Give my love to Louise.' Shortly afterwards he died.

Carlotta did not attend the funeral and so did not see Pete break down in tears.

Enzo, in fact, was so moved by Pete's caring nature that he gave him the use of Dino's apartment in Maranello not far from number 11, Via Trento Trieste, the team headquarters and where Enzo had his office. It was during this time that Pete learned to speak Italian and would often accept Enzo's invitation to join himself and his wife, Laura, for meals. His marriage to Louise – that had caused a brief hiatus in the mon ami mates relationship – made no difference to Enzo. The Signora was of the same feeling and told her husband that Pete had married a perfect woman, a *speciale donna*, both domestic and faithful, irrespective of her theatrical career of which the strictly Catholic Laura was slightly dubious.

It was not long before Louise wrote to her parents in praise of the Ferraris: 'Mrs Ferrari insists on going everywhere with me, which is funny because I don't understand a word she says, but we get along. Enzo has even offered to let us have their villa in Rimini. It's huge with a balcony that runs the whole length of the house. They are wonderful to us. And guess what? They invited us for a meal and Laura got up to present me with a fabulous three-diamond ring. What a life!'

Carlotta could be excused her jealousy of Louise, knowing of her closeness with the Ferrari family. It showed in the jokey comment she made about her: 'Look at her, the way she dresses for the pits, wearing the latest Levi jeans turned up to just below her knee or that great bulky overblouse above those skinny pants.' She added with a grin, without knowing that Louise was a star of Broadway, 'Who does she think she is?'

Carlotta was also wrong in believing that Enzo had given Tavoni orders to 'set up' Hawthorn and Collins' cars with more care than that afforded to Luigi's car. In fact, Enzo had instructed Tavoni to give equal attention to all four cars so that each driver could compete with his teammates on an equal basis.

In all this Romolo Tavoni remained diplomatic and tactful in his dealings with the four drivers. He was not a top engineer, nor even an experienced mechanic, having been Enzo's personal secretary until 1957 when he was transferred to his new job as team manager. This puzzled many people, but, of course, the Commendatore was famous for his odd decisions. The answer was simple. He had stopped attending races and required someone suitable to stand in for him. He had felt that Tavoni was the only employee he could rely upon to carry out this task with thoughtful care, always with an eye to protecting the good name of Ferrari, of course. Enzo had stepped back from the sport he loved, had stopped attending races – he had been a racing driver himself in his youth – because of the opprobrium heaped upon him by church and press for the number of fatalities that the Scuderia de Ferrari had sustained in recent years. He had been labelled as 'an angel of death' in losing such stars as Eugenio Castellotti, Alberto Ascari and Alfonso De Portago. After the latter's fatal accident the press and ecclesiastical attacks had intensified.

It was because of this pressure that Enzo had placed Tavoni as a buffer between himself and the press with the task of putting the best gloss on any tragic accident. For added value Enzo had asked him to feed him personal information about the members of the Scuderia. He was an employer who believed that the more you knew about people the better placed you were when things went awry.

In this role Tavoni was not only his 'spy in the camp' but also one of the world's first spin doctors. With such matters lying in the hands of the capable Tavoni the Commendatore would be able to remain aloof and unavailable for comment. But, at the same time he intended that Tavoni was to be the fall guy should there be any repercussions or brickbats flying around.

Until now, Tavoni had no great crisis arise within the Scuderia to challenge his powers of diplomacy or call for his expertise in dealing with the press. However, this most sophisticated of team managers had simply no idea of how to deal with the crisis in the life of Luigi Musso as presented to him immediately prior to the French Grand Prix. As he busied himself with his check list, he worried about how he would present the bombshell to Enzo.

\* \* \* \* \*

The preliminaries to the race start were underway. Mike, Pete, Luigi and Taffy were busy in the motor home getting into their racing clothes. Then they turned their attention to their vizors. It entailed sticking see-through plastic strips – one on top of the other – over the aperture designed for seeing through when the filth thrown up by high speed racing clouded the rest of the vizor. It was a matter of ensuring that each strip curled outwards so that it could be easily grabbed and torn away when it became difficult to see through.

As soon as they were ready Luigi manoeuvred himself so that he would be next to Pete at the rear of the group of drivers as they strolled into the pits. Detaining him with a touch on his arm Luigi spoke in rapid Italian. Pete had difficulty at first, but then realised what he was being told. In shock he immediately agreed to lend Luigi any prize money that he won. But, of course, he could not speak for Mike.

Carlotta joined Luigi watching Pete confront Hawthorn in the pits.

'Luigi wants us to share the winner's prize money three ways.'

'Eh?' Mike laughed briefly. 'What's he on with? It's our private' – He broke off, his voice drowned by the blare of an engine starting up. He allowed Pete to steer him back into the paddock for a quieter word.

'It's like this. A business partner wants his money back. He says that if we can agree to lend him our winnings it could buy him the time to pay off the rest he owes. This guy's threatened to kill him. He's really scared, Mike.'

Mike, realising that Pete's concern was genuine, hesitated. Should he bend a little then Pete, the nice guy, would hurriedly take it as an agreement and tell Luigi that his worries were over. That annoyed Mike. It was simply not in his sporting code to disturb a racing driver's concentration before a race. Mental attitude was everything. He may have been an amateur driver in terms of finance but in racing mode he was as professional as Stirling Moss. There was also a difference between Mike and Pete in their view of the Italian people. Unable to talk their language, he failed to understand them, unlike Pete. On the credit side he could easily have told him that all his prize money was spoken for, pledged as it was to Jacqueline and Arnaud Michael. It was unfortunate that he felt he had to keep it a secret as it would have changed Carlotta and Luigi's view of him. His blunt refusal to help Luigi only served to confirm their opinion, that Hawthorn was uncaring.

'Pete,' he said. 'We're not a charity. It's between us. How do we know what he says is true? I can't believe it.'

'I just feel it's really serious. Let's do it. Just this once?'

'No. I can't.' Mike shook his head. 'I just can't' – he raised his voice against the mounting engine noise. 'Mate, listen. Tell him we'll talk to him afterwards, yeah?'

Reluctantly, Pete nodded and went back to Luigi to place a hand on his arm. He spoke in a sympathetic manner.

'Luigi. Ci dispiace possiamo parlare e più tardi?'

Luigi stared past Pete's shoulder at Mike, paused, then strode quickly to put his arms around Carlotta, comforting her.

'Non preoccuparti,' he whispered in her ear. 'Sara bene.' He stuffed cotton buds into his ears, placed both hands on her cheeks and kissed her.

'Vincero la gara.' I will win.

He walked abruptly past Mike to go back into the motor home for a few moments, to sit alone, close his eyes and try to focus on winning the race.

'Vincero la gara…vincero la gara' he kept intoning. If he kept repeating the mantra, confirming that he would win the race, then he would win the race.

'Vincero la gara.'

He left the motor home, grimly determined to do or die.

In the Vanwall motor home Stuart Lewis-Evans and Tony Brooks – an English dentist by profession – were just about ready when Mike came to the door holding out a brown leather body belt. 'Here you are Stuart. Sorry I forgot to bring it back.'

'It's okay Mike. I've got another.' Stuart took back his body belt. 'Did it do the trick?' He referred to the race at Monza.

'Yeh, but bloody hell my guts ached after that. It was a roller coaster.' Mike hesitated then poked his head inside the motor home. 'Have a good race Tony.'

Tony Brooks smiled back. 'And you Mike. Cheers.'

Stuart stood in the doorway and watched Mike walk back to the pits, wondering why he had needed two body belts. Had it anything to do with the spots of blood that he had seen in the paddock toilet after Mike had vacated it during the final practice session?

Stuart Lewis-Evans was born near Luton in 1930. After leaving school in Bexleyheath he served a three year apprenticeship at Vauxhall Motors, did his National Service as an army despatch rider and, with his father 'Pop' Lewis Evans, started motor racing in 1951. He was as popular a figure on the circuit as any. A small man, no more than 10 stones in weight, he was often portrayed as lacking stamina, although he undertook endurance racing with enthusiasm. Away from the track he was a lively character, full of fun, enjoying family life to the full and modest to a fault about his considerable, sometimes hard won, successes. He was conscious of his small, thin frame and his tendency to allow himself to be bullied. For that reason he could sympathise with anyone in trouble, especially the underdog.

Like Pete Collins, he was caring.

But he was also careful. His loyalty, after all, lay with the Vanwall team.

\* \* \* \* \*

A race official wearing a blue blazer, stood in the middle of the track facing the lines of cars. He wore a leather band, etched in gold and blue lettering, around his arm. A signboard held above his head notified the drivers and everyone else on and around the grid, as well as the spectators in the grandstand, that the '15 minute' countdown had begun. The mechanics were carrying out checks and last minute adjustments to their cars. As usual they were surrounded by a crowd of people. Apart from the mechanics and team managers were invited guests, family and friends, photographers and press, the excitement building with each passing minute.

Amid all this Mike sat calmly on pole position, wearing his favourite blue spotted bow tie and his regular 'race uniform' of green gabardine jacket, white trousers cut short at the ankle, and his familiar blue helmet. He glanced across his front row.

On the outside was Harry Schell in the BRM, created by the legendary Raymond Mays and one that many British fans would have loved to have seen Mike occupy as it was now owned and run entirely by Rubery Owen, a manufacturing company in the West Midlands. Harry caught Mike's eye and gave him the thumbs up. Mike responded and then looked at Luigi, next to him. He was staring grimly ahead, his hands tightly gripping the wheel, a bad sign thought Mike, suggesting that mentally he was ahead of the race.

The 'Two Minute' klaxon was followed by calls on the Public Address system ordering everybody to clear the grid. The last to leave after the 'One Minute' klaxon were the mechanics, scurrying back into the pits.

At the fall of the flag the cars went on their warm up lap and were back between three or four minutes. Then came the race. It was Harry who stormed into the lead. Mike trailed for a few seconds but then, as the pack of cars roared down the hill towards Thillois, dived in front to lead Harry, Luigi and Stirling into the corner. Any pain that he had experienced before the race had disappeared, caught as he was by the thrill of the chase.

At the end of the first lap Pete moved into second place with Luigi immediately behind. Having set a new lap record Pete hurtled past the pits, was approaching the right hander but was horrified to find that his brake pedal had stuck. Instantly he made rapid gear changes to prevent the engine from exploding. But the car was out of control, spinning round and round in a screech of burning rubber. On its final revolution it righted itself to point towards the corner.

Louise went into shock at seeing a pall of dust rise over the braking zone. She only started to breathe again when calming signals were made at her by Tavoni, meaning that Pete was okay.

The cause of brake failure, Pete discovered as he got back into the race, lay in the mechanics failing to secure an air scoop that had come adrift to lodge under the pedal. On his next lap he hurled the offending lightweight piece of metal into the pits. Louise gave a nervous laugh in relief as it sailed over her head.

Of some concern to Mike was that Pete's 'incident' had allowed Luigi to move into second place. With Mike in his sights it galvanised him to drive with abandon, braking late and running wide on cornering. This was not the 'normal Luigi' of the race track, more like the behaviour of a novice who had no idea of the dangers he was creating for himself. This was not 'ten tenths' driving either – when a driver pushes a car to its ultimate potential – his was 'eleven tenths', spelling danger.

After seeing Luigi escape yet another disaster Mike knew that he had been telling the truth about his desperate need for money and hoped that he would not get so close that he might take both cars off the track. There were no run-off areas, no acres of sand, no catch fencing, merely the hard concrete, walls, fences, ditches and other hazards that bordered a public road. A high speed crash would almost certainly result in injury, if not death.

It was inevitable Mike thought. Christ, it was going to happen! Jesus ! There! Luigi went over the limit once more, this time narrowly avoiding a wall.

On the 10th lap Mike approached the right hander after the pits, hit his braking point accurately, then nicked the short gear lever through fast down changes. Halfway around the corner he made rapid up-shifts to power out. As his line straightened only then did he glance in his mirror. There was no sign of Luigi's car.

All he could see behind was a billowing cloud of dust.

On the next lap, as Mike approached the pits, he saw that Luigi's lap board was no longer on display. Then he spotted the medical helicopter hovering over the corner ahead. But on rocketing past he saw no evidence of a wrecked car.

On the 12th lap Mike saw the helicopter rising into the air. After a pause, it dipped its nose before shooting forwards for a turn into the afternoon sun.

But still no sign of Luigi's car. Nor could there be, it having disappeared from the circuit, propelled over the wall and now lay part buried in the soil of a farmer's field, some 20 metres from the wall.

\* \* \* \* \*

The National Anthem played for Mike as race victor. A big crowd of British fans stood to attention watching Mike on the podium with Stirling in second place and Taffy in third. Normally, having won a Grand Prix, Mike would be surrounded within seconds and signing autographs by the dozen, but this time he ignored the pack of cheering British fans who rushed across the track, and raced into the paddock to find sanctuary in the Ferrari motor home.

There, he grabbed a tumbler of water and sat down. Trembling and in pain he pulled out a Tylenol tablet and popped it into his mouth, taking a swig of water to wash it down. Then he lay down exhausted and soon fell asleep.

When he awoke he found Pete with Louise and Taffy. Mike looked up at them, his expression strained. He noticed that Louise had red rims around her eyes. 'Are you alright Mike?' she said.

'Yeah. Bugger about Luigi.'

'They're examining the car,' said Pete. ' What do you think?'

'No need. He was over the limit, all the way.'

'Not understeer then.'

'No way mate.' Mike peered at him. 'You worried that we turned him down? Is that it?'

'I dunno.' Pete shook his head, looking troubled. 'I just don't know.'

Tavoni came into the motor home, paused and then said, 'The scrutineers say nothing is wrong with the car. We know that Luigi had business worries. All we will say is that he was desperate to win. Everybody in Italy wanted him to win.'

Louise said, 'How is he, do we know?'

'No.' Tavoni shook his head. 'We go to the hospital soon. Carlotta has shock and the doctor is with her.' He left the motor home, heavily burdened.

Louise went to the stove. 'Does anybody want tea? Pete? No?'

She looked down at Mike.

'Tea Mike?' She spoke gently.

Mike nodded and put his head in his hands. 'He was right over the limit, every turn, every turn. I knew it would happen. Christ.'

Harry Schell poked his head inside the motor home. 'Jeez, Mike. You okay?'

Mike nodded.

'Luigi, what the hell was he doing!'

His tone brought their attention.

'Carlotta was raving, shouting your names,' he said. 'Calling you something. I dunno. Like she was crazy.'

'But Harry…' Louise looked at him in sympathy but raising her eyebrows in a touch of reproof. 'She loves Luigi you know. She really loves him.'

After Tavoni had supervised the loading of the race cars and garage equipment into the transporter he made a second telephone call to Enzo informing him that the scrutineers had found no fault with the car and that any doubt about it having understeer beyond its normal limits had been scotched by other drivers and witnesses. Tavoni also reported that he was taking Carlotta to the hospital with instructions that the whole team should follow after a decent interval. He had to ensure that she heard any bad news first.

He also made it clear that no member of the team, mechanic or driver, would be permitted to talk to the press about the accident.

\* \* \* \* \*

When Mike, Duncan, Pete and Louise arrived at the gates of the hospital, its windows were shuttered against the sun, giving the building an austere and forbidding appearance. Followed by the mechanics they entered the silent and dark corridor, its walls and floor tiled throughout so that each footstep brought an echo.

Tavoni approached them out of the gloom, his face grave as he shook his head. Before he could speak the echoing sound of a woman sobbing in grief came from a room at the far end. It was Carlotta.

In Mike's head the sound grew louder. Then other sounds intruded, accompanied by flashes of light. 'Jesus,' he whispered to himself fearfully.

Pete turned to look at him.

Mike looked around in terror. The corridor was dark, sinister and closing in. A photograph on a wall had an awful significance, not because of what it portrayed but for what it was, an oppressive thing. He stumbled back down the corridor trying to take in huge gulps of air, but his lungs were already at bursting point. Beads of sweat stood out on his forehead, his face a deadly white. His brain was paralysed, processing nothing. Gone was logic or any kind of thought. Out of the building he staggered, desperately seeking rescue, nearly falling over as he lost his footing on the outside steps.

In the hot sunlight the full horror struck, his mind flying in a chiaroscuro of light and dark flashes amid images of decapitated bodies, torsos spurting blood, torn bits of flesh and flying limbs.

It took Duncan and Pete all their strength to grab hold and contain him. Somehow they managed to bundle him into the car. Pete drove at speed back to the hotel while Duncan held him by the shoulders to prevent him repeatedly banging his head on the back of the driver's seat.

It was only when he reached the safety of his room that Mike's fear diminished and he began to breathe normally once more. He was given a tablet to calm him down. Soon, his mind returned. He was back, lying on a bed with his eyes wide open and thinking of only one thing, the realisation of what had happened and its cause.

Despite all the counselling by Duncan, all the arguments in his favour from the motoring press and in spite of the race authorities exonerating him from all blame, he knew that the panic attacks had only started after the Le Mans disaster. Was it not obvious that the deepest part of him believed – no, knew – that he was responsible for the deaths of over 80 people and more than a hundred injured? Luigi's death had simply been the trigger that plunged him into such distress. It was punishment for what he had done, was it not? He could have saved Luigi by showing generosity but had not.

Duncan and Pete waited cautiously for him to speak.

# **Chapter** Three

By late afternoon the Via Trento Trieste was still sunny and busy with traffic and pedestrians. At number 11 the office blinds were down. A cigar smouldered in an ash tray. In the adjacent room Enzo stood before a shrine dedicated to the soul of his lost son. Burning candles stood on either side of a large colour photograph of Dino who had died aged 24. In the soft candlelight Enzo's silvery, swept back hair contrasted with his dark suit and black spectacles, the latter being a sign of his constant mourning these past two years.

He stood up and with a slight tremble of the fingers lit a fresh candle for the soul of Luigi Musso, said a short prayer and then returned to his office where he flew up the blinds with a rattle, then sat down and picked up his cigar. Nervously, he placed his elbows on the desk and clenched his hands together until the whites of the knuckles showed.

When Tavoni had telephoned him at 4.10pm with the news of Luigi's death a chill had swept throughout his entire body. He had employed only one Italian driver in the four man team in order to lengthen the odds against him being the next fatality and it had failed. Tavoni would not be able to field all the abuse that would surely come his way from the church and the press.

Although his report had given Enzo some relief – the official race scrutineers had examined the wreckage and had not found any fault with the crashed car – the outlook was bleak. It did not matter that a number of witnesses had testified that Luigi had been driving like a *lunatico*. He knew that he would be accused yet again of slaughtering a son of Italy as entertainment. Once more they would seize on the tragedy as proof that Scuderia Ferrari was run by a ruthless dictator.

In reality, Enzo's fear of opprobrium was not the sole reason for him not attending races. The truth was a little more complex and tinged with darkness. The facts were that he had ceased to be a motor sport enthusiast after he built his first racing car. From then on it was his cars that he really loved.

Of course, he mourned their crashes, not as much as the drivers who died, but mourned them none the less. In the dark glamour that cloaked motor racing in the 1950s any tears that he shed for the dead were genuine, but in relief he would turn to his cars. Few people knew that following Mass on Christmas Day and Easter Sunday, rather than join his family, Enzo would go to unlock his showroom and spend an hour wandering about them, alone. They had stayed faithful to him all his life and he would remain faithful to them.

He looked at his watch. It was 5pm.

After Tavoni and the team had visited the hospital Carlotta was taken back to the hotel where Beba, Fangio's girlfriend, and Lulu Trintignant, the wife of Maurice the racing driver, had taken her into their care.

But no sooner had they shepherded her into the room than she ran for the open window, had one leg over the sill and was about to throw herself out only to be stopped at the last moment by the two guardians grabbing hold and hauling her back. Enzo received the report on that incident from Tavoni at 4.45pm. Only 15 minutes had elapsed since her suicide attempt. He had noted the time and details of both phone calls in his diary.

Enzo looked at the telephone as it rang yet again, composing himself before answering. It was, as he expected, Tavoni. His news was that Carlotta had escaped Lulu and Beba and had tried to stop him as he was about to drive back to the race track.

'She went crazy. She wanted to kill Hawthorn and Collins – and you, Commendatore.'

At that Enzo shivered at the image of her flying savagely at his face with her red painted finger nails. Or would it be something far worse? He gave instructions that on no account must Carlotta travel back to Italy unescorted.

After the call he opened the file on his desk and read the notes that Tavoni had made about her during the last year. Carlotta's love affair with Luigi was recorded as 'hot blooded'. Their sex life had been animalistic. Even in company they would sit holding hands, pressing soft flesh with forceful thumbs, wincing and enjoying the pain of denial. This lust for each other was matched by their closeness in everything they did. She was there for him in every aspect of his life. Their love transcended their bodies. It was as passionate in its spirituality as it was carnal. They prayed together and they lived for each other.

Enzo read Tavoni's notes of her complaints during the season. She was known for her temper and so Tavoni had not made any personal comment, merely recorded what she had said. The last entry was made just prior to the French Grand Prix. She had demanded to know why it was that the Englishmen were being favoured at the expense of Luigi and was Enzo aware that he was demoralised by it? Was it not a miracle therefore, with such poor back up, that before the race at Reims he stood only five points behind the championship leader, Stirling Moss? And only two points behind Mike Hawthorn? Could any man in the Scuderia, including the Commendatore, deny that Luigi's achievement was a triumph, given his handicap, and should he not be looked upon – and treated – as the world champion in waiting and not Hawthorn or Collins?

Enzo closed the file, could read no further. He had met Carlotta twice at team parties. She would always get into some sort of argument, for that was her nature: combative. In any confrontation she would never retreat but instead jut her chin forward aggressively, her dark eyes flashing. Or she would reinforce the point she was making with a jab of her fingers before stalking away with a feisty toss of her glossy black hair.

Enzo put the file away in a lower compartment of his desk and thought of the bad deal that fate had dealt him. It was all so unfair. He had done his best to avoid another Italian driver being killed in one of his cars, but look where it had got him. He had tried to increase the odds against it happening. Even then he had been accused by thousands of Ferrari fans that he was being unpatriotic in not having more Italian drivers in his team. He felt a stab of anger at his countrymen who praised him when he was victorious and kicked him when he was down.

A tear in his eye caused him to blink. He took off his spectacles to wipe it away. It was not a noble tear. This time it had been sparked by self pity. He looked at his watch to find that there was one hour left of the working day. But he would not leave until later in the evening to avoid any door-stepping photographers or reporters. His secretary had strict instructions not to put through any calls other than from Tavoni or Luigi's immediate family, definitely nothing from Carlotta. His head servant at home had the same instructions and in addition was ordered to lock the tall and heavy gates that led into the tree shaded courtyard of his large, dark and secluded house.

\* \* \* \* \*

Mike lay on his bed in the Hotel du Nord, propped up by his pillows and sipping brandy from a toothpaste tumbler. Pete sat on the side of the bed, drinking beer. Stuart leant against a wall listening to Duncan addressing Mike and Pete.

'It's not your fault, either of you. How were you to know? If he had begged Stuart or Stirling to share the money he'd have got the same answer. He got himself the chop.'

Mike nodded. 'Too right. Just before the race starts he's asking me for money! Should I have let him overtake, to let him win? No! No way.'

There was a tap at the door. Stuart went to open it.

It was Bernie Ecclestone, a racing driver on occasion and owner of the part-time F1 Connaught Team and who was having difficulty raising the money with which to compete. Bernie was a small man but focused and intense, like Stirling. He had come to sympathise and pay his respects.

After him came Juan Manuel Fangio. Having completed his last race the world's greatest driver could look forward to retirement freed from the dangers that had taken away Luigi, as well as a number of other friends.

Duncan welcomed him inside the room. Mike got off the bed, only too willing to greet the true Golden Boy of motor racing – and in more respects than one. Juan Manuel Fangio had been World Champion five times and runner-up twice, a man for whom honour and integrity counted more than anything. He was fortunate in that he had completed seven full Formula One seasons but had only suffered one serious accident. He was also lucky at Le Mans. If Mike had braked a split second later it could easily have been he who had died, instead of the Frenchman, Pierre Levegh.

After the disaster Fangio had offered Mike his sympathy, but had no idea how badly he had been affected by it. Few people did.

Mike's close circle of friends had managed to keep it secret. Had Fangio known there might have been a greater warmth in the partial, hesitant embrace that he shared with him.

But then Fangio turned to the man for whom he held the very deepest respect and to whom he was deeply indebted. In 1956 Fangio had joined the Ferrari team as a replacement for Alberto Ascari who had been killed. It was his good fortune to have as a teammate, Pete Collins. At the season-ending Italian Grand Prix, Pete and Fangio had both started the race with an equal chance of winning the World Championship. When Pete came into the pits for a tyre change with only 15 laps to go, he found that Fangio's car had broken down. He then made what could arguably be regarded as the most generous act in the history of sport. He had offered the Argentinian his car, allowed under the rules, causing Fangio to stare in astonishment and then demur. But Pete had been insistent. Fangio was the much older man and would be retiring soon, he said, whereas he had many years left in which to claim the crown. Fangio had quickly hugged him before climbing into the car, unable to believe his luck. Pete had literally handed him the world championship.

In gratitude, after winning the title, Fangio had tried to compensate Pete in various ways, promising to do all manner of things, but Pete had waved them away, saying he had been only too happy to help a real gentleman of motor sport. And the Italian newspapers had been only too happy to hail Pete's extraordinary sacrifice. Having lambasted Enzo for his number of fatalities they now showed equal zeal in showering praise upon his English driver who was a 'signore maschile' possessing 'a true nobility, style, class and a sporting dignity that was unmatchable in any sport'.

While Mike was 'in recovery mode' Carlotta Mancini sat in her room with the curtains drawn. In the semi darkness she studiously repeated – and kept repeating – phrases in English taught her by a sympathetic barman. She was patient with herself, unusual for her, but in this instance what she would say aloud had to be intelligible and understood.

* * * * *

Later, since the English drivers were not travelling home until the next day, Duncan, Pete and Louise dragged Mike into the hotel garden, still holding a half drunk glass of beer. Far better than moping around in his room, they said. They had wanted to take him to Bridget's Bar but Mike had no wish that night to mix with other team members.

Unfortunately he found that the garden, with its geometrical lay out of lawns, low trimmed hedges and lack of flowers was less than soothing. It even made him feel a shade nervous. Fearing it might trigger off another panic attack he lowered his gaze. At his feet lay an empty tin can, a short distance from an ornamental stone wall.

He kicked it automatically, the can hitting the wall and bouncing back. He kicked it again without any change in his sombre, set expression. It clattered back again. It became necessary to keep kicking it. His accuracy failed at the moment that Carlotta came out from the hotel to confront them.

Instead of the can striking the wall it spun off in the direction of Pete who thought Mike had recovered by the act of kicking it towards him. And so he 'passed' it back to Mike with a relieved smile on his face. It was this smile that Carlotta first saw as she stepped out on to the terrace in search of the two of them. But her interpretation of the scene she witnessed was different to its reality.

She was watching Hawthorn, who was holding a glass of beer, playing football with a can that he had emptied. And Collins was grinning. And only five hours after Luigi's death, their teammate.

'You – I hope you die!' She screeched out the words she had learnt so well and now invested with real venom.

Mike, Pete and Louise turned to stare at Carlotta, her face lit by the lowering sun, her hands clenched, her face ugly.

'Bastards. When you die I will be happy!'

\* \* \* \* \*

Tavoni was in a room at the hotel answering questions from the press. One reporter asked if the Commendatore would listen this time, to the church in Rome? Wasn't it time for the barbarity to cease?

Tavoni, speaking for Enzo, said that the Scuderia office as well as the factory were closed in respect, but wanted to remind the reporters that Luigi had died doing the thing he loved. The Commendatore would be making an approach to Carlotta Mancini with a view to helping her in any way he could. There would be a Funeral Mass said for Luigi to be attended by everybody who worked for Scuderia Ferrari. Work was continuing at the factory to make Ferrari racing cars safer with each passing year. He hoped that circuit owners would start to improve their security and safety features. There would come a day, he pronounced, when death on a race track would become a rarity. In the meantime the press and public should respect the brave men who gave their lives in providing such high risk, but widely supported entertainment.

Mike, alone in his room, was packing his case for the next day's journey home. Halfway through his task he checked himself.

Until now he had given no thought to his victory or the fact that he currently shared, with Stirling, first place in the world championship table.

It suddenly occurred to him that if he could surmount his troubles – plus a bit of luck regarding Stirling's unreliable Vanwall – he could tackle the remaining five races in the calendar and emerge as the winner. However, at that moment the prospect gave him only a twinge of satisfaction, submerged as he was in deeper, more worrying concerns.

First, on his return home, he had to make another visit to Guy's Hospital for yet another examination. He feared what might be discovered about his one functioning kidney. How he wished that he had escaped the gut wrenching Monza 500.

Mixed in with this depressing thought was his dread of more panic attacks accompanied by frightening fantasies. 'Post-traumatic shock' as a diagnostic term had yet to be coined and his medical notes referred to him as suffering from 'transit situational disturbances'.

He had been free of such attacks for over a year and so their reoccurrence had shaken him to the core. Following the tragedy he had had so many attacks that he had entertained the idea that he was one of those classical heroes 'of whom the gods wish to destroy, they first make mad'. But he was now even more convinced that it was, indeed, his underlying guilt that was responsible. And now, what would Luigi's death, something he could have prevented, do to him? The pity was that he could not talk about his fears with Duncan. It would be too embarrassing. The two of them shared a love of life's pleasures but laughed loudly in the face of personal adversity, big brave men as they were. Showing weakness of spirit was just 'not on'. Their core relationship was built on a mutual sharing and celebration of the convivial life in a healthy and carefree world of cars, booze and women. It also involved a degree of shared cynicism and deprecation of anything sentimental – and that included religion and all its connections. Guilt, that is a sense of responsibility for one's physical actions, was a 'legit' subject but indulging in 'talk of conscience,' touching such abstract notions as God, sin and punishment was right off limits. Duncan would find such talk excruciating and that in itself deterred Mike.

There was a knock at the door. It was the return of the slightly built and sensitive Stuart.

'Mike. Can I have a word?'

Mike let him into the room.

'I forgot to tell you about your panic attack.' Stuart looked at him sincerely and in concern. 'A friend of mine has them and he carries a paper bag with him all the time.'

Mike blinked.

'What you should do when you feel it coming on is breathe into the bag and then breathe in what's inside. It's the carbon dioxide.'

Mike was slow on the uptake.

'In a panic attack your brain says you need oxygen but it's tricking you. You've got too much. You're hyperventilating. You need the opposite. You need carbon dioxide.'

'Bloody hell. Really?' Mike shook his head. 'It really works?'

'Yes.'

'Jeez. You certain?'

'Yes. Well it does for him.'

'Bloody hell. Thanks.' Mike paused. 'If it was only that simple.'

'What? How do you mean Mike?'

'Life – or death.' He gave a wry smile.

Stuart paused, choosing his words. 'Mike. I know you had them after Le Mans, all that stuff. These things happen. It's not something you can control. Look, if there's anything I can do, just tell me. Okay?'

Mike hesitated – was Stuart really someone who he could trust to share his problems? He needed to talk easily about the things that troubled him. It would not be a case of 'a trouble shared is a trouble halved' as it was more like a cancer within, something that he had tried to excise mainly through pleasure seeking. The trouble was, he thought, that Stuart actually looked priest-like with his long pale face and earnest expression…

Suddenly Mike found himself talking. 'I've got a kidney problem. I've had it for years. That's why I needed the body belt at Monza.'

There was a pause before Stuart spoke tentatively. 'I saw a spot of blood in the loo after you'd been in. Was that…?'

'No. Not me.' Mike lied quickly, 'I've got a problem but it's not that bad. But keep it to yourself. Only Duncan knows.'

'Mike.' Stuart spoke gently. 'I'd no idea. I promise you I'll do anything to help.'

Mike liked Stuart – everybody liked Stuart – but he was small and thin, and so keen to please. He suddenly regretted taking him into his confidence. Why had he talked about his illness when it was his conscience that bothered him? If the secret got out he would be finished in motor racing. Jesus, he felt he was going to pieces. He had to stop it, regain control.

'I'm going to have a kip Stuart. Sorry. Do you mind?'

'No you do that Mike. I've got a sleeping pill if you want it? It's a barbiturate knock out. Guaranteed.'

'Er…no. I've got some. Thanks. I hate taking pills.'

Stuart smiled and nodded. 'Okay. Look after yourself. See you later.'

After Stuart had gone, Mike sat down at the bedroom dressing table and looked at himself in the mirror. He was glad that he had not used Stuart as his confessor. He did not want to owe him any more than he did already. And Stuart was a touch 'weedy' despite his courage. That was the latent bully in Mike talking. And his ego.

He opened a drawer to take out a sheet of writing paper and picked up a pen. Quickly he began to write notes about those things that he could not talk about with Duncan, far less with Stuart. There was no 'eureka' moment, but in writing down phrases like 'Death is nothing', 'absolute zero', 'as you were before you were born', there came an order of ideas that acted as a key to his darkest and most troubling of thoughts. It took an hour to complete. Then he read the whole piece again, checking as he went, anxious not to miss a strand or a link that welded together a piece of logic that, on completion, was so liberating that he sat back and grinned at his reflection. He decided that he would take it everywhere he went and, if needed, would take it out and re-read. It was his bible. It would bring comfort in adversity.

He was so exhilarated that it allowed him a moment of remorse about Stuart, then rang him on the room intercom. He invited him to spend a couple of days with himself, Pete and Louise, in Monaco.

Stuart was delighted. To be thought of as Mike's friend boosted his self confidence, something that he had always lacked. On the track he had to put in a greater effort in steering the car than most drivers, given his slender arms and small muscles. Cockpits were not moulded to the body, as they would be in later decades. They gave him plenty of room in which to rattle and roll. All of this added up to a considerable handicap. Pound for pound, it could be construed that he was braver than most drivers. But, of course, the modest man that he was, he failed to recognise it.

Mike took a bath, dried himself and put on his gentleman's apparel of corduroys, Harris tweed jacket, bow tie and ratting cap. To complete the picture he clamped his favourite pipe between his teeth and then went out to join Pete, Louise and Duncan in the bar before dinner. Shortly afterwards Stuart appeared and Mike bought him a drink. He had an idea regarding him, all to do with that bed soaking in the hotel in Reims.

\* \* \* \* \*

'My advice is that you finish with motor racing.' The consultant went on to tell Mike that there was no direct evidence that the right kidney was failing but it would be advisable to get out as soon as possible.

'I've heard there are kidney transplants…' Mike's question was in hope, not expectation.

'Yes, but in America, not here. They work for a few months then fail. There's no way of preventing the body rejecting them at the moment. In time possibly we may have the answer.'

'There's these machines…dial' machines?'

'Dialysis. Yes. Some hospitals have got them but they're so few that all the kidney patients who need them have to share them. Lucky if they get one session a month. That's not enough.'

Mike returned home in a sombre mood. The medication he was now taking, called Prednisone, was an oral corticosteroid. One of its side effects was that it could create a moon face by fattening out facial tissue. Sooner or later it would be so evident that the press would be asking questions. It gave even more urgency to solving his dilemma.

He thought that he had lost his focus, had allowed himself to be knocked off course by events. Should he give in to them, cosseting himself against his illness? Or should he make the final, irrevocable decision to continue racing? The consultant's latest prognosis left him with no alternative but to decide now. He was tempted to quit but then came the thought that all the pain he had suffered in reaching this moment in motor racing would then be made pointless. Then he considered the counter argument. If he had done himself irreparable damage through racing – the consultant thought he had – then to retire now would not in itself repair that damage and so he might as well continue. For God's sake – he kept telling himself – there are only five races left, that is all. Come on! Five fucking races! Buck up!

At that moment he had a clear vision of his situation. Given Stirling's bad luck with the reliability of his cars, Stirling was not the favourite to win the world championship. He was. He imagined the wreath of laurels placed around his neck. There would be that everlasting moment of glory. And then came that thought – again – of his mother whom he loved and knew he had treated so badly. Becoming world champion would mean that all her financial worries would cease. This would have a double benefit in cleansing at least part of his conscience.

It was these thoughts that made him drag out his testament, the folded piece of writing paper that he had brought back with him from Reims. He read the affirmation: 'Le Mans was not my fault. Luigi's death was caused by a crook. I have no reason to be scared of anything.'

It helped. So long as he kept repeating these things and stopped worrying about the inner terrors he would be fine. He made up his mind. The die was cast.

To hell with it. It was 'balls out' time.

\* \* \* \* \*

'Are you really alright darling?'

It was Winifred, standing in the kitchen doorway, looking weary. He stood up and went to her, putting his arms around her and giving her a kiss.

'I'm great, mum.'

'Good.' Winifred was a sensitive woman whose life had been wrecked by her marriage to Leslie, an unfaithful husband. She had hated him even more because he had lured her only son into risking his own life while making out it was fun. In the early days she had accompanied them both to the race tracks, had pretended to enjoy the experience while hating the noise and smell of racing cars, their screeching brakes and burning rubber. There was that awful moment when, at Oulton Park race circuit in Cheshire, a D Type Jaguar had overturned and she had watched it shoot past until it came to rest with the driver trapped underneath. Minutes later he had emerged covered in blood and although it came from skin lacerations it was a sight so shocking that she had almost vomited.

From then on she could not bear the thought of Mike risking his life and had refused to have anything more to do with it. Since then she always made a note of the British time for each race in which Mike would compete. Five minutes before its start she would remove the telephone from its cradle or leave the house until it was all over.

There was another reason why she loathed her husband. He had ignored Mike's congenital kidney disease that she had suspected was exacerbated by motor racing. He was a selfish man and Mike seemed to have taken his place in ignoring the distress that he caused her. Even so her mother's love had remained undimmed. She knew her son. She could detect or see, where others could not, a slight fattening out of his features.

'Mike. Are you sure you're alright?' She gave him a tired smile.

'Yeah, I'm terrific.' He gave her another kiss and said that he was travelling to Monaco with Duncan. Stuart would be already there, staying in a hotel near Casino Square. They would have some fun together.

Winifred gave him a bright smile and when he was gone broke down and cried.

The following night Mike stepped off the boat with Duncan, Pete and Louise. He had told Duncan that the consultant had cleared him for the rest of the season and he was feeling great. Together they would visit the Tip Top Bar which stood down the hill on the left-hand side from Casino Square. It was the racing driver's favourite watering hole and a place for carrying out practical jokes. Someone once returned to his car that he had parked outside and found it upstairs. Harry Schell, of course, had been involved.

The Bar was packed. The centre of attention, as always, was good old Mike, at his cheeriest best. He stood with his back to the bar, lighting his pipe, his bow tie straight and level and engaging in loud conversation and laughter with Duncan, Taffy, Phil Hill an American driver, Pete and Louise. Watching eagerly, enjoying their contact with the famous, was an assortment of hangers-on.

With a couple of beers inside him, Mike began to sing the bawdy rugger favourite. Soon they were all singing it:

'Four and twenty virgins came down from Inverness and when the ball was over there were four and twenty less, singing balls to your father, backs against the wall if you've never been shagged on a Saturday night you've never been shagged at all!'

Even so, his face flushed, the booze inside him and the camaraderie of the moment undeniable, he had time to note a girl with large breasts and pouting lips standing with her friend near the door. He recognised her as one of the 'camp followers' who travelled around the Grand Prix races in Europe. He decided he would make his approach shortly.

In the meantime Stuart had walked into the bar and joined Mike's gang. He did not know the verses, but could sing the refrain. When the song ended, Mike put an arm round his shoulder, then gripped him, drawing him in close.

'Glad you could make it my little friend.' From somewhere behind him he whipped out a hose pipe that was connected to the tap in the bar. 'Regarding that bedwetting in Reims old mate, I'm returning the favour.'

With that he wound the hose pipe round Stuart's waist and stuck the nozzle down his trousers. Mike gave a signal to Duncan who had moved behind the bar near to the tap. Mike gave it a quick short burst. Stuart yelled out. Everybody laughed. The bar was in an uproar.

'You've pissed yourself you dirty little man!' shouted Mike.

'You bastards,' said Stuart, clutching his groin. 'That deserves a drink!'

'Yeah, here's the second.' Another quick burst, Stuart yelling. The gathering shaking with mirth.

'Oh dear look at the state of you. Let me wash it off,' Mike roared.

* * * * *

Afterwards, back on board *Mipooka*, Mike knew that what had been enjoyed in the bar that night was to be the last of his hell raising. He was determined to devote himself to the one thing that mattered, winning the world championship. He had to be more like Stirling in his attitude, self disciplined and strictly focused. Leaving his cabin he went on deck to join Pete for a hot chocolate provided by Louise. Without talking they lay back against the wheel housing to stare up at the great amphitheatre that was Monaco, glistening and twinkling in its wide bands of serried steps fading upwards into the mountains.

The next morning he went for a walk, telling Pete and Louise he needed the exercise and wanted to go alone. He decided that he would suggest to Pete that Louise might be better off in America pursuing her stage career, enabling both men to concentrate on their racing, not good living. He believed that Louise could be persuaded on the grounds that she had received a cable from Peter Ustinov in New York offering her a part in a stage play that he had written called *Romanoff and Juliet*.

However, in this regard he had a problem. Louise was frightened of not being at the track when Pete competed. She had an illogical belief that her presence would protect him from accident.

He walked passed the tree-lined section of roadway that formed the pits on race day, then along the quayside before turning up the hill to stride into

Casino Square. Soon it was downhill, past the Tip Top Bar to pass eventually through the long curving tunnel. Then came the long descent alongside the harbour, all of which formed part of the Monaco race circuit.

At the bottom he came to the spot where a year previously there had been a huge shunt in which Pete had crashed into a barrier with Tony Brooks braking to avoid him. That had caused Mike to crash into him, slamming his car into the barrier to end up alongside Pete's car. They had climbed out laughing.

It was also the spot where, three years earlier, Alberto Ascari in his Ferrari had crashed into the water, having missed a chicane. He survived. Mike drew a convoluted lesson from all of this, telling himself that he had not been killed and neither had Pete. And Ascari had died during testing, not racing, as had Eugenio Castellotti. Apart from Alfonso de Portago and Luigi there had not been any recent deaths of Ferrari drivers in actual competition and those surviving would remain lucky, would they not?

He could not help reflect, however, on what Denis Jenkinson had written in the latest edition of *Motor Sport* magazine about the increasing calls for more safety on the track. His response was to write:

'Everyone keeps crying out for "Safety, more Safety" and yet every day man-made machines are made for reeking death and destruction all over the world.

'If man dabbles in dangerous machines he must pay the consequences. No one has ever been forced to watch a motor race nor has any racing driver been forced to become one. Real he-man motor racing is practically extinct. In the end one can foresee everyone wrapped in cotton wool and I hope they all choke to death in their own safety.'

Mike respected 'Jenks' and – until the last year – would have agreed with him entirely, as might have Stirling Moss. However, for the last five races of 1958 Mike fervently wished such danger would disappear.

He walked round towards the swimming pool complex opposite which was moored *Mipooka*.

Louise was in town shopping when he came aboard. Pete was on deck fiddling with some equipment when he saw him. 'Mon ami!' he cried out. Then, on his way to the galley, called out 'Bubbly?'

'No.'

Pete was checked by the command. His head poked above deck.

'What's up? You alright?'

'Yeah, let's have a cup of tea. I'll tell you.'

In the galley Mike watched the kettle boil and told Pete that he had seen the doctor about his stomach. 'It's all this late night eating with Louise,' he added.

'Why Louise?'

'You know she likes eating in the best places and late at night. It's all rich stuff.'

It was true. But Pete was uncertain whether to laugh or take it seriously.

But Mike was serious. 'I mean it. I'm quitting after this season. It's my last chance to win the championship. I've got to stay in shape. And it's good for you too mate. You want to win the championship don't you?'

Pete looked at him. 'Have you got something wrong with you? You have, haven't you.'

'It's called Reflux,' Mike said. 'It's acid that comes back at you after you've eaten.'

'Reflux. Sounds like an exhaust bodge up.'

'That's what it is. Got to stop it getting back into the engine.'

Pete regarded him with a cynical smile. 'Oh yeah?'

'Yeah. Honest mate. Cross my heart.'

'Fancy fish and chips? Or a curry?'

'No. Milk and a biscuit.'

He was thinking how best to approach the matter of how they might persuade Louise to remain in America for the rest of the season but spotted her walking towards the boat. She was carrying a shopping bag.

It was not the moment.

# **Chapter** Four

Even as Mike sat in the Ferrari coach on its way to the funeral, he observed people walking ponderously, not talking, their heads bent to the slow toll of the muffled bell.

It was as though the whole of Italy was in mourning.

Once in the Cathedral of San Giovanni, he stared at the coffin in which lay the body of Luigi Musso. It was raining outside and what light filtered through the tall stained glass windows was murky at best. He worried that the simple philosophy worked out in Reims and which he thought might save him from more panic attacks, was rubbish.

He had construed that death was a mere nothing, meaning instant oblivion, absolute zero. He had tried to convince himself that there was no punishment in an after life. It was based on the premise that 'you' never existed before 'you' were born and therefore 'you' would not exist after you died. All baloney. The punishment, he now knew, was already taking place – in life.

It threw everything into the melting pot, even his decision to act in a professional manner during the two or three months left of the season. Until his arrival home from Reims, despite the worries over his state of health, he had managed to keep on an even keel. But on arrival at Heathrow in the company of Duncan and Stirling he had once again been plunged into a vortex of confusion that produced the first symptoms of paranoia. Convinced that there would be at least one reporter 'out to get him' he refused to take part in a press conference with Stirling. But after Duncan argued that it would be disastrous for his reputation, being one of the two Brits level on points at the top of the world championship table, an unprecedented situation, he finally gave way. Nevertheless, he insisted that he would not answer 'dodgy' questions.

After a few innocuous questions came one from an Italian reporter he had not seen before. 'Did he think his chances of winning the championship were greater now that Luigi Musso was no longer in contention?'

It was asked innocently enough, but Mike was suspicious and felt his pulse rate quicken. He knows that I rejected Luigi's plea…He suggests that I killed Luigi for my own ends.

Mike had stared hard at the questioner, mumbled some sort of reply and then looked away, asking for a more 'sensible' question.

As they drove home through the rain and the darkness, he told Duncan that he had been close to walking out of the press session as they were 'against him' in favour of Stirling.

As the funeral bell ceased and the strained silence began, he felt increasingly afraid. Churches always had that effect on him, but it was worse being immersed in the heavy atmosphere of a funeral service for the man he could have saved. When the Ferrari contingent were given their pew seats he had found himself sitting behind Carlotta, who had arrived on her own and as far away from Luigi's widow as possible. She wore a black veil in defiance of the family, all of whom had chosen to ignore her.

It was pure coincidence, but he felt her threatening presence.

He regretted not discussing his worries with Stuart. He saw him – could imagine hearing him – offer his earnest reassurance: 'Come on Mike, let's be serious, of course there aren't any malevolent spirits. It's nothing more than sheer bad luck. There's nobody out there trying to get you.'

But now, as his eye travelled up the huge pillars of the cathedral and its soaring walls, he felt their impact and was dismayed. He lowered his gaze to the coffin, his eyes locked on its gleaming case.

Pete had wanted to save Luigi.

As he heard the shuffle of the Priest's feet and that of his Acolytes approaching the altar it was as though they were coming for him. It was not only the *Corriere delli Alpi* newspaper that had condemned him, but also the Pope. He had not been named in his speech but how else could he interpret it? Was he not part of the evil that was motor racing? He embraced its deadliness. The torment intensified as the Priest and Acolytes came into view, their black vestments contrasting with the whiteness of their hands and faces. As they approached the mahogany coffin, richly carved and decorated with brass handles, he became fearful that the whole world was taking part in the great solemnity of the Mass, all eyes fixed on the casket.

Pete was the Good Samaritan. Anyone else was the Devil.

He tried hard to think in a straightforward logical manner to escape being sucked down into another panic attack that he felt was imminent. But his conscience would not allow it.

It did not matter that the police and official enquiries into the Le Mans disaster had come out with a verdict of it having been nothing more than a 'racing accident'. Three years later his conscience told him otherwise. He was, without doubt, being punished. And who was giving out that punishment? Himself.

He watched the Priest and Acolytes performing a ritual to the accompaniment of a childish sob from the family pews. A black pall was opened and spread reverently over the coffin. His pulse rate quickened further, his breathing becoming faster and more shallow. Luigi was the only one who could forgive him and he was gone. How else could he be saved? Despite the warmth in the cathedral he felt cold. The service would never end. He was trapped. It did not occur to him that his depth of conscience was evidence of a good man embroiled in a terrible misfortune.

Suddenly he saw the coffin disappearing underneath the cloaks of the Priest and his Acolytes, stretching like linked black umbrellas around and over their prey. Terror struck. He had to escape, but there was no escape, trapped in the centre of a tight row of people. Remembering, he stuffed a sweaty hand into his pocket. Was it there? Oh dear God, let it be there. He dragged out a small brown paper bag, stuck a finger inside to screw the paper around it, rammed the roughly fashioned funnel at his mouth, breathed into it and then inhaled. Breathed out and inhaled. Breathed out and inhaled.

He sat back in his pew, his head back, his eyes tightly shut.

The Introductory Rites ended as his panic faded into a steadying dullness of mind. When he reopened his eyes the dreadful vision had gone.

The choir began to sing *I am the light of the world*.

He closed his eyes again and was calm…

The Introductory Rites being over, there followed the Office of the Dead in which prayers were offered. During them Mike kept his eyes closed in fear that he might see something that would trigger another attack. He tried to breathe slowly.

His eyes were still closed as the next stage of the Mass began, The Gospel. Consequently he failed to see that candles were being distributed among the congregation, that is until Pete nudged him to accept one.

His eyes took in the flames around him giving a welcome spread of light, providing a spark of warmth and hope. He noticed that some individuals, lighting their candles faster than others, would turn round and offer their flame to the person sitting directly behind.

One such was Carlotta Mancini.

As she turned she froze at Mike. The candle that she held cast an upward light on her veiled face, producing shadows that turned her features into a mask. Her eyes remained steadfastly locked on to his as she paused, then deliberately and carefully blew out her candle, yet still offering it him. Her eyes were dry and there were no other signs of grief, hatred delaying it.

She quickly turned back.

It was not her face or its lack of expression that had driven a stake through his heart. It was the recognition of the symbolism of her action. In denying him the light she had cast him into darkness.

'Lux perpetua luceat eis' the Priest intoned.

Let eternal light shine upon them.

She had extinguished that light. She had silently passed on to him Luigi's mortality.

He breathed once more into the bag.

# **Chapter** Five

Carlotta was the last person Enzo wished to confront after Tavoni's report on her vitriolic outburst against all things Ferrari. And so he was relieved to hear that the burial ceremony was to be purely a family affair. However, not able to escape the Funeral Mass that preceded it, he made sure that he would be sitting in an aisle seat ready for a quick get away once it was over.

But one problem had remained, the *famiglia scia*, the wake, that was to follow the internment and of which protocol and expectation demanded that he be present. He solved this dilemma by offering to donate a sum of money that would more than cover the cost of food and refreshments while sending his deepest regrets that he would be unable to attend, his excuse being that he had an urgent and entirely unavoidable meeting back at Maranello that affected the future of his company.

The letter arrived at the family home together with the cheque, thus defusing any hurt that he might otherwise have caused. Carlotta would not have been invited, of course, but he was wary of being trapped. What if she decided to barge her way in and subject him to a verbal onslaught? That story, plastered all over the national press, would have been disastrous and something that not even Tavoni could easily have handled.

Enzo hurried down the steps of the cathedral in relief. He had taken the trouble to park his car as close as possible to the front of the building. As he approached it he became excited, almost erotically, because this was his real love. His blood red machine, with its logo of the prancing horse on its front, excited him as would the most beautiful of bodies. It was also, literally, stripped for action.

The fabric top had no inner liner and the only 'extra' was a small heater, but in terms of potency – 'Gloria all'estremo' – the car's performance matched that of his Dino racing cars. This, the 250 GT California Spyder, was his most recent creation, the best ever in the history of the world's most glamorous marque. It was so sought after that it filled the factory order books for the foreseeable future, not least in the American market, hence its name.

As he slipped into the driver's seat Enzo congratulated himself. He could have been chauffeured to the funeral that day but then he would have lost the prospect of one of the drives of his life – not as great a loss as that of Luigi, of course, but it was an opportunity, even in this saddest of times, not to be missed.

Nevertheless, as he fired the engine he felt a pang of remorse. Luigi's body had not yet been lowered into the ground. He decided he would pray for him on the journey home. On the autostrada though, he would not worship anything other than what he sat in, flat out at 225 kilometres an hour.

\* \* \* \* \*

Mike left the cathedral dreading the wake that was to follow. Like Enzo, he would have found an excuse to give it a miss had he not been forced to go on the Ferrari coach that day. After the Mass it was intended that it would take the whole Ferrari ménage to the family home. Resigning himself, he decided he would stick close to Pete and Louise, hoping that he would not have another panic attack. He was also worried, like Enzo, that Carlotta might be present on the solemn occasion. It was a measure of his state of confusion that he overlooked the obvious. Would Signora Musso have invited the woman who had ruined her marriage?

In the event the 'family Musso' commemorated their long departed husband and father in a rather stiff and formal ceremony that lasted no more than an hour.

Just before they left, Mike's attention was caught by a beckoning gesture from Pete who was standing in the hallway, out of sight of the family and guests. He joined him.

Pete held an opened newspaper in his hand bearing the headline: 'MUSSO MORTE PONE QUESTIONE', which he translated as 'Musso's Death Puts the Question'. He quietly précised the news story. It said that Luigi had been heavily in debt to some businessman who had links with the mafia and was desperately in need of money with which to pay him back.

'Anything about us?' Mike asked anxiously.

Pete read on. 'No,' he concluded. 'It just says he tried to win the race for the prize money and that may have caused him to crash.'

Mike's head dropped in relief.

'Mike.' Louise took his hand. 'You are coming back with us to Monaco, aren't you?' She spoke with a tone and expression that made it more of a plea, than a question.

He hesitated.

'Mike. I saw you in church. You had another attack didn't you. I saw you with the paper bag.' She gave him a sad smile.

Mike, driven by the fear of having another embarrassing breakdown in public, was keen to fly home at the earliest opportunity and remain there until the first practice for the British Grand Prix at Silverstone on 17 July. But Louise had anticipated this.

'Don't worry. You'll be alright with us. I'm going to mother you, I promise.'

She squeezed his arm. That, and her gentle insistence won the day.

They left for Monaco that afternoon. Pete was driving and they arrived at *Mipooka* late at night. Mike was utterly exhausted, the long journey having added to the stresses of the day. He went straight to his cabin, took a pain killer and fell fast asleep.

About the same time Carlotta sat in the flat she had shared with Luigi. There were no lights switched on, the only illumination coming from the monochrome television screen.

She had seen brief shots of the funeral service on the television news, but now saw in her mind's eye something much more detailed than that which the grainy footage had depicted. Fixed in her memory was Hawthorn's expression as she had turned round to face him during the Mass. It comforted her. She had other plans for him.

\* \* \* \* \*

Enzo Ferrari, 250 miles away in Maranello, listened to Tavoni's account of the wake by telephone. He was satisfied by what he heard, especially the absence of Carlotta.

But then he asked if Tavoni had read the newspaper report about Luigi's death being the result of trying to win the race in order to save himself from debt. Did Tavoni have any idea who might have given the newspaper the story?

Tavoni had not read the newspaper report but answered immediately. 'Carlotta.'

It was obvious. Whoever had given the story to the reporter would have done it with some sort of revenge in mind. It had to be someone on the inside of the Scuderia or closely attached.

Who else but Carlotta? She had witnessed poor Luigi make his desperate pleas and had been seen with tears in her eyes at him being turned down.

Okay, asked Enzo, so why had the news story not referred to Hawthorn or Collins? Surely she would have told the press about them refusing Luigi's request? That was the whole point of her giving the reporter the news story, wasn't it?

Tavoni suggested that the likely explanation was that the newspaper's lawyer would have deleted that part of the report.

After a short pause Enzo concurred with him. Of course, under the Italian Penal Code the offence of libel if committed by the press, was punishable by imprisonment of six months to one year, plus a fine. They would not have dared take the risk.

After the call Enzo went to his cigar box that stood on a dark and heavily decorated side table and chose a Romeo y Julieta cigar. As he set light to it he decided that Carlotta was a dangerous woman on the loose. Somehow she had to be corralled.

But what do you do with an enemy like her? Naturally you do not give more offence by accusing her of talking to the press. No, the best way, was to condition her through the emotions. In her case, having lost the one man in her life through a tragedy involving the Scuderia, there would have to be some sort of compensation offered. *Naturalmente.*

He sat down in his winged leather armchair and placed his silvery head back in contemplation. He sat there for 20 minutes in deep thought, at the end of which time he had made up his mind. His main aim would be to neutralise her hostility.

He decided that he would telephone her the following day. He would assure her that he understood her feelings. What had happened to her and Luigi was a great tragedy and she had every right to loathe everybody connected with his death, including himself. Oh, but how he would tell her of his own grief at Luigi's loss. It had given him sleepless nights. How could he be expected to sleep? He prayed for him every morning and night, of course he did. Then he would mourn that the church would, no doubt, be attacking him again, for which he had no defence, except to give his word that he did everything within his power to ensure the safety of his drivers. He prayed for their safety before a race and during it. What more could a man do?

At that point, if the conversation was going well, he would invite her to Maranello where she 'would be offered something in the way of compensation'. He would not specify what form it would take. Secrecy was all important and the security of his telephone line could not be trusted. He was sure that this bait would succeed in bringing her to see him.

On her arrival his first act would be to invite her into his shrine room for prayers. Afterwards he would take her to lunch where he would use all his charms to defuse her latent anger.

When she accused him – as she was sure to do – of having issued orders that the Englishmen be favoured over Luigi he would adopt a hurt look. In order to prove his sincerity he would say that he was willing to give her double the money that Luigi would have received from the Englishmen had his plea been accepted. He would stress, of course, that money could be no compensation for her grievous loss but everyone in Maranello was anxious to help. The Scuderia was a family, a caring family. Everyone wanted to show her their deepest condolences and friendship eternal. They had asked Enzo to pass the message urging her to think of nothing but the future.

Finally he would say that if he had upset Luigi in any way it was not by design, but by his lack of communication with the team. Nevertheless, he was determined to find out the facts of the case. She would be told that Tavoni could not have informed him of Luigi's plea for help as that had occurred far too late, just prior to the race. He had only learnt of his dilemma after the accident. Had Tavoni been in a position to put Luigi's case to him the day before the race he would have loaned him all of the money required.

Enzo, satisfied with his plan of action, examined the ash tip on his cigar. He would not forget his own, personal security. He would ensure that his secretary was present when Carlotta first came into the office. As soon as he sensed that he was safe, only then would he dismiss him.

His thoughts then turned to Carlotta herself. He was driven by the memory, on the few times they had met, of her sex appeal as being almost irresistible. She would be aware that he had a mistress. She knew of his reputation and so the very act of visiting him would show that she was either totally unafraid or not averse to any overture he might make.

But he would not touch her sensually in any way, not on the first visit. It might be seen as too presumptuous and her anger rekindled by it. No, she was a woman in mourning and as such she would be treated. He decided he would embrace her on her second visit, wait to feel her relaxing body against his, the slow movement of her head as she calmly looked up into his eyes.

\* \* \* \* \*

The next morning Monaco was lit by hot sunlight as Louise, wearing a shirt and Levis with braces and the trouser legs rolled up below the knee, walked from the boat and climbed upwards towards the Boulevard Princesse Charlotte. It was a routine walk that she did most mornings in case any letter, cable or telegram had arrived from her agent or Peter Ustinov regarding the new play. She walked into the American Express office but was surprised to find that the duty clerk was not the usual man on duty and so did not recognise her.

'Good morning. Have you anything for Louise King please?' She gave her stage name.

The clerk reached into a pigeon hole, withdrew a telegram and handed it to her.

It was from Peter Ustinov asking if she could fly over to New York for the next two or three days. She thought about it and sent a negative reply. She had promised Mike she would look after him and she would keep her word. Then she remembered. 'Oh, is there anything for Collins? You've also got me registered as Louise Collins, also the boat *Minooka*.'

The clerk consulted his files then looked in the pigeon hole marked with a 'C'. There was a telegram addressed to Mike, 'care of Collins'.

Back on board she handed the telegram to him. It was from his mother and was very brief. 'Come home. Stop. Urgent. Stop' was all it said.

It meant that Louise would go back to the American Express office and send a cable to Ustinov accepting his invitation.

\* \* \* \* \*

Mike sat in the living room with Winifred, having had a row, both in the taut silence of its aftermath. She had told him that the family doctor had been contacted by the consultant at Guy's Hospital because he had failed to stop Mike from racing and thought that a mother's emotional appeal might reap a better dividend. He had shown her nothing short of anger and frustration at being dragged home for something less than the house burning down or the garage catching fire.

He had been expected home in one week's time anyway to prepare for the British Grand Prix, hadn't he? It was all so pointless.

It was not pointless to Winifred. It had been coming on for a long time, she said. His living on a boat in the Mediterranean was stupid when he was ill.

He felt sickened by it.

Suddenly Winifred said, 'I mean it Mike. If you don't stop I shall tell the FIA about it.'

Mike stared at her in miserable disbelief. He had already told her that he was nearly there, that all he had to do was complete five more races. In any case his left kidney had survived five years of racing, and since the right was hardly touched and because he intended to retire after those races why quit now? And here she was threatening to end his career by 'shopping' him to the FIA. He shook his head in despair.

Then she spoke. 'You're like your father. You're very selfish Mike. You never once consider what I go through when you're racing, do you?'

Mike dropped his head and sighed.

She relented and put out a hand. 'I'm sorry. It's my fault. I should never have let your father set you off on this. I hated it all from the start, but I couldn't stop him. He knew about your condition and still he carried on.'

She thought about what she had said.

It brought a quiver to her lip, stimulated by resentment and self pity. 'You know that you were dragged into it for his own reasons.'

Mike grimaced at her. 'What? Mum, I don't know what you're talking about. I wanted to race. I would have done it without dad. What – ?'

'Oh no. No Mike.' She cut him off with a sharp gesture. 'I'll tell you the truth now. We know you wanted to be a racing driver. But he encouraged you because it gave him opportunities.'

'What?' Mike stared at her in bewilderment. 'I don't get it...what...?'

'I'm talking about his extra marital activities.' Her mouth was tight and she shook slightly, enjoying her bravery. 'His own purposes.'

There was a silence as Mike continued to stare at her.

She spoke decisively and rapidly. She was not hanging back any more. 'He got you racing so he could go to all these paddock parties where he could pick up whoever he fancied. He sent you away to school for only one thing. Not for you but himself, so he could bring his women here to an empty house when I went to visit my mother. He was nothing but – '

She broke off as Mike stood up and went into the hallway, picking up his dog's lead.

'Come on Grogger' he said harshly and banged the back door as he left the house.

It was while he was out taking his dog for a walk that the telephone rang. It was Pete from Monaco.

Winifred was cautious. 'He's not in at the moment Pete. Is it important?'

'Well, we're worried. Obviously. We just hope there's nothing really bad happened.'

'Oh, not like that. No, well...' As she struggled to think up some appropriate story a surge of resentment flooded in. Why should she be made to feel as she did, wretched and worried as she had been for years, making excuses all that time?

Pete continued. 'Is there anything we can do to help?'

It suddenly occurred to her that, indeed, he could help.

It came out dramatically, a deliberate challenging statement meant to shock. 'He's got a kidney disease, Pete. He's had it from when he was born.'

She paused for its effect to be felt and then launched into the whole story and ended by emphasising her plight as a mother.

There was no immediate answer.

'Pete? Are you there?'

'Yes. I'd no idea. That's terrible.'

'Pete? If he won't listen to his doctors and certainly not me, would you – could you – talk to him? Try and show him, try to…?' She broke off emotionally.

There was a longer pause before Pete spoke, 'Louise has gone to New York about a play. I could fly over, see Mike before she gets back. I'll try and get a flight tonight'.

'Oh yes, please. Pete, I can't tell you how grateful I am.'

'Just one thing. I knew he'd got something, but not – are you absolutely certain it's that serious?'

'Certain?' Winifred said in disbelief. 'Pete, I'm at my wits end. You've no idea what I've been going through all these years.' She began sobbing into the telephone.

Pete waited until she had calmed down a little. 'Winifred.' A pause. 'Winifred?'

'Yes, Pete.' Her sobs died.

'If I get over can you promise not to tell Mike I'm coming?'

'Of course I won't. Thank you, thank you…'

'I know what he's like, you see.'

'No I promise. Thank you so much.'

She was about to say goodbye when a thought struck her.

'Oh Pete. I have to tell you something.' Her voice trembled but she spoke doggedly. 'If it doesn't work and he still keeps on racing, I'm going to inform the FIA of his illness. They'll stop him. I'd rather you did.'

That evening Mike drove over to Tilford Green where he met Duncan in The Barley Mow. He told him about Winifred's threat to 'shop' him to the FIA if he refused to stop racing. They would cancel his racing licence as a result. He felt that he could not stay under the same roof as her, the pressure on him so intense.

Duncan was saddened by the news. Had he not listened to Winifred's anxieties over the years, helping her to cope? And now all his good work seemed to have come to nothing. He took a drink from the colourful ceramic tankard that was kept specially for him behind the bar. 'Mike, just tell me one thing. Can you cope to the end? Be honest. How fit are you to carry on?'

'Top notch. No problem,' Mike lied into his beer, then saw Duncan looking at him with a glum expression. 'Yeah, I've told you. The doc hasn't ordered me to stop. I'm okay.' He grinned at Duncan's uncertainty. 'Honest, Scout's honour.'

For the first time in their relationship Duncan sensed that Mike was not telling him the truth. Lamely he asked what Mike wanted to do at that moment.

'I want to get away from mum for a couple of days. The pressure's terrific.'

Duncan thought it a good idea. 'Right. Tell you what we'll do, we'll bunk off for a few days.' It would get Mike relaxed, ahead of the first practice day at Silverstone on the following Thursday. The break would be good for Winifred as well, he thought.

'Where?' said Mike.

'What about Dublin?'

'The Guinness Brewery. Great.'

'Yeah, we can go there one afternoon. One problem. All you get is one drink, gratis.'

'Oh bloody hell. Oh, okay, we'll do that. Then where? Do you know Temple Bar?'

* * * * *

It was 8.30am the following morning and Winifred was appalled. Pete had told her that he would arrive at Heathrow at 9am and would ring from the terminal building as soon as he was able. And now Mike had just told her at breakfast that he was going away with Duncan for a few days.

'Where are you going?' she said, hiding her panic.

'Dublin. Duncan's picking me up about 10 o'clock. Why? What's the matter?'

She thought quickly. 'Mike. I forgot to tell you that Pete rang and said he might be coming over today. Louise is in New York and –'

'What?' Mike interrupted her. 'Why didn't you tell me? Pete could have come with us!'

Winifred said quickly, 'Could you hang on till he rings? Maybe he can.'

She left the room. It was not fair. She was trying to save her son from himself and had been forced to act miserably and cruelly. When would it all end? Pete rang at 9.30am. She answered and quickly handed the receiver to Mike in the hallway. 'It's Pete.'

It was arranged that Pete would go with Mike and Duncan to Ireland. He had just gone through Customs and made the request that they gave him 'an hour or two to get sorted'.

Relieved, Winifred went to lie down in her bedroom, exhausted. At least Pete knew the situation. For the first time in years she felt she could relax. Pete would fix it. He would choose the best moment to make his plea. He was sincere and tactful. How she wished Mike was more like him. She turned over and cried into her pillow, as much for herself as Mike. She dreaded what might happen if he found out that she had told Pete of his illness, something she had faithfully promised not to do.

* * * * *

Carlotta arrived at the Ferrari headquarters at 11, Via Trento Trieste by taxi, having made most of the journey by train. The secretary, a young serious looking man, escorted her into the room and waited for instructions. She was still wearing black, but they were fashionable 'weeds' that accentuated the lines and curves of her body. She was without a veil. Enzo moved towards her, removed his black spectacles, gave a slow and sympathetic shake of the head and took her hand. He patted it, *così delicatamente*.

'Carlotta. I am so sorry,' he said.

He flicked a glance over her shoulder. His secretary had moved into position behind her. 'So sorry. Please. Come and sit down.'

He ushered her into an armchair at the side of his desk. As soon as she sat down the secretary followed to stand behind it.

Enzo was relieved to note that she sat down in a steady and controlled movement, showing tension, not anger. He picked up a silver cigarette box and presented it to her without taking his eyes from her face. She returned his gaze while reaching into the box. Enzo clicked his cigarette lighter. She leaned forward and bent her head to draw on the flame.

Enzo sat down. 'How are you now? Grief is such a terrible thing.'

'You know what I feel,' she said. 'Luigi died because he was not treated well as he should have been.' She sat back and blew a cloud of smoke into the air. Enzo was surprised and encouraged by her calmness. Did it mean she was going to angle for some rich compensation? He gestured at the sheer impossibility of taking on all the ills of the world.

'If I'd known I would have acted immediately. I do not promote jealousy. That is the ruin of business. Why should I want a driver to be jealous? Or get so desperate that he has to drive over the limit? An accident in itself costs thousands of pounds in the lost car having to be replaced. If I'd known about the money I would have gladly loaned it to him. Of course because it would have saved him and saved me.'

He gestured again, but this time in a show of humility. He was anxious not to argue. He spoke in a softer tone. 'Carlotta. I have lost a driver who was the symbol of Italy. I would never draw down all that fire on my head. You have lost the man who you loved and would have married you.' He went on to assert that in feelings alone, Luigi's accident had terrible repercussions – and not just inside the Scuderia. 'Every engineer in my factory is set back by it. Some could not come to work the next day.' He broke off to put a hand to his head as if in pain.

Carlotta remained hard faced. 'But you knew about Hawthorn and Collins. Their agreement to share prize money. The way you favoured them.'

Enzo shook his head vigorously and raised the palms of his hands. 'No. It was a private deal between them. And I favoured nobody. Did you talk to Romolo?'

Her eyes searched his face as she drew thoughtfully on her cigarette. And in that moment he knew there would be no violence.

He stood up. 'Please, let us say a prayer for Luigi.'

He dismissed his secretary with a flick of the eye and then went to stand by the open door to the shrine room.

She hesitated. She had heard of Enzo's shrine to his dead son.

Enzo remained standing, his arm pointing towards the room, a sad smile on his face.

With a slight curl of the lips she slowly placed the cigarette in the groove of an ash tray, stood up, looked at him with a faint trace of cynicism and then approached the room. Only then did his arm drop as he followed her inside.

The shrine had been added to by more candles standing either side of a new photograph, that of Luigi. It had been selected and blown up from an original that showed him happily chatting with Pete and Mike in the pits.

Before Carlotta could react Enzo quickly made the sign of the cross and said, 'Absolve, we beseech Thee, O Lord, the soul of thy servant Luigi, from every bond of sin, that being raised in the glory of the resurrection, he may be refreshed among the Saints and Elect. Through Christ our Lord, Amen.'

It forced her to respond. 'Hail Mary, full of grace, the Lord is with you, blessed are you among women, and blessed is the fruit of your womb, Jesus. Holy Mary, Mother of God, pray for us sinners, now and at the hour of our death, Amen.'

She crossed herself and looked at Enzo. A tear was running down his cheeks. He took out a handkerchief while giving her the wearisome smile of the man who tries to do good, one who remains steadfastly honest and magnanimous in the face of adversity. He took her arm, gently.

'Let me take you to lunch,' he said.

He took her to The Cavallino in Via Abetone Inferiore, much frequented by the factory engineers and mechanics, as well as the test drivers. Of late it had started to exhibit the Scuderia's memorabilia and consequently Ferrari fans had started to visit the restaurant where Enzo's table gave him predominance over all the other tables. The waiters, having been warned in advance of

Carlotta's appearance, showed her due sympathy in their deferential body language and sympathetic murmurs before escorting them to the table.

Enzo ordered fried Ravioli with a glass of Valpolicella. Carlotta chose a Caesar salad with water only. It served to strengthen his fear that she intended to manipulate him in some way. By going to the press with her story? It was time for him to take the initiative. He was framing a question that would deflect her from making any such threat when he caught her studying him with a suspicious smile.

'Did you cry for Luigi, or your son?'

'What?' He froze, drink in hand.

'Before the shrine. I'm an actress, don't forget. Someone told me you were a very good actor when needed.'

Enzo stared at her in shock. She had divined the truth. His ability to turn on a tap had been learnt unwittingly, had nothing to do with studying the 'method', a technique taught to actors, by which they could draw on past emotional situations to elicit genuine emotion rather than simulate it as traditional acting demanded.

He thought quickly, knowing that he had to show sincerity.

He put his head forward and spoke slowly and quietly. 'I cried for all my drivers, Alberto, Eugenio, Alfonso…and now Luigi. Dino, my son, only died two years ago and just to stand there, with their photographs together…' He pursed his quivering lips tightly. 'Perhaps I cry first for Dino. But Luigi, God bless his soul, was…'

He broke off to quell his rising emotion.

Carlotta was impressed, aware that she was getting nowhere and his ego had been punctured enough.

'You brought me here to talk about compensation,' she said and left it as a flat statement.

He nodded, then looked at her seriously.

'Yes. I would like you to work for me. Personally and privately. I will pay you, not to work but to watch and listen.' He dipped a piece of bread into a shallow dish of olive oil and balsamic vinegar.

'First I will pay you a lump sum, double the money that Hawthorn won at Reims.' He took a sip of wine. 'I want you to report back to me. I need eyes and ears to keep the team on its toes. The more I know the better I plan. I like to keep people competitive, off the track as well as on. And it will stop any more jealousies as a result because I will know everything about everybody.'

She continued to stare at him. Was he genuine or so stupid that he thought she was so naïve? Luigi had warned her that Enzo was a 'cunning old fox' and never to believe anything he said. He always had some ulterior motive she had been told.

'What is my job to be called?' She took a sip of wine.

'Nothing. You will work for me, personally.'

She glanced down at her hand on the table. It was now covered by Enzo's hand. It confirmed her suspicions that his next move would be amorous.

He said quietly, 'I need a woman's sensitivity. I need to know personal things. Feminine things. Chit chat. Gossip. Tit bits of information so I can make sure never again is there any bad feeling. Would you do that for me? Be my spy?'

He ran his fingers up to her wrist before letting his hand slip away. Sensing her stiff reaction, he regretted breaking the promise he had made to himself that he would not make any overtures on their first meeting.

'How much will you pay me?' She lifted her eyebrows at him.

'I will pay for your hotels, travel and food.' He paused. 'And 7,500 lire a month.'

'I'm to be your spy.' She gave him a thin smile.

'Yes. But a secret. Between the two of us.' He paused. 'On one condition.'

'Wait a minute.' Her chin jutted forward, her eyes flashed and her mouth opened in shallow breathing. 'Do you expect me to sit in the pits or in the motor home with the two men who killed Luigi?'

Instinctively his hand went to hers again. But this time it was a clasp of reassurance. 'Please. Take my word, they didn't. Listen. If it works out I will pay you more. I will pay you a lot more if you treat Mike and Peter as your brothers and not your enemies.'

She eased herself back in the chair. A thought struck her. Was this not what she wanted? To be close to Hawthorn and Collins so as to extract her revenge in the best way possible?' But then she thought that Enzo would have taken into account her animosity towards the English drivers. He would undoubtedly give strict instructions to Tavoni to be careful with her. But there would be opportunities, she felt, sometime, some place. The food arrived and Enzo felt content at having achieved his aim in corralling Carlotta inside the Scuderia, far less dangerous than having her on the outside seeking revenge. He had asked her to be his spy because that was something that Tavoni had failed in. He had tried to explain to him that a presentation of what seemed useless bits of information could add up to something significant, that a close scrutiny of the behaviour of his Scuderia work force could be used to prevent any future inter-team conflict. So far he had failed to appreciate or admit that his employer was a brilliant interpreter of inconsequentialities.

However, he recognised that Tavoni was a dignified man and would have considered the task as beneath him. Enzo, in fact, was pleased that the way was cleared for Carlotta, the sexiest of spies, to be taken on to his pay book. But he had to tread cautiously. It might, he thought, take some time getting her into bed. He might have to be more generous.

A hand touched his shoulder. It was a local businessman, a friend.

Carlotta smiled to herself as Enzo stood up to shake hands. She thought of the reporter she had fed with the story of how the actions of Hawthorn and Collins had killed Luigi. His inability, because of the fear of libel, to have his story published could now be looked upon as fortunate. She would not have been taken on to Enzo's payroll had that occurred, she had realised. Nevertheless, he would make a very good contact if the need arose. There might be things she could keep back, information that had a price.

In the matter of Luigi's treatment she did not believe Enzo's protestations of innocence. She needed compensation for that, not just in the form of money but also *dello spirito*. What better way than to frustrate his desire for her?

She decided she would gain revenge as well as money by keeping him on tenterhooks, by keeping her distance.

But, right now she could look forward to being at the British Grand Prix, a week away. There was a way of extracting revenge that no one, other than the victims, would notice, she thought. It gave her dark pleasure.

# **Chapter** Six

Duncan chose Dublin as an ideal getaway because he knew that Mike had fond memories of the place. It was there, in June 1951, when he had started his racing career driving a 1500cc Riley Sprite to victory in his first road race, run over 10 laps at Phoenix Park. A month later he won the Leinster Trophy race in combative style that brought him acclaim in the pages of *Autosport*. Duncan thought that the trip down memory lane would prove relaxing and he had put a telephone call through to make contact with one or two members of the local motor racing fraternity who had bid Mike a fond farewell after his last race in the old country.

Duncan had another reason for choosing Ireland, one out of nostalgia, for it was in County Cork where he had been born. His chosen method of travel was also out of sentiment. They would travel by the Liverpool to Ireland ferry.

As the boat approached the estuary leading to the port of Dun Laoghaire there was only one passenger out on deck, unsurprising given the unseasonably cold wind and spots of rain. Pete stood at the boat's railing wearing a raincoat and cap, wishing he was with Louise sitting on deck in the warm air and sipping Vesper Martinis, instead of being stuck on what had been a long, tense and miserable sea crossing. He gloomily took in the fine sweep of Dublin Bay and the weird, conical silhouettes of the Wicklow Mountains to the south. It would have been all so exhilarating had he not been so downcast. So far he had met with failure. He had tried to winkle Mike out of the bar, but it was impossible since a ferry boat was his idea of paradise. He had spent so much time drinking rounds with his admirers that it was hardly the place in which to discuss matters of life and death. And if on-board hospitality was any indicator Pete could not envisage it happening in the next couple of days either, seeing that Mike had persuaded Duncan to line up a 'gentle tour of Temple Bar' where most of Dublin's 'character' pubs just happened to be situated. Even if Mike was separated from his drinking pals there would always be Duncan at his side killing any chances of being buttonholed for any heart to heart stuff. Pete actually felt relieved to be temporarily freed from his obligation as it had given him time to step out on deck to assess the situation, instead of continuing to lounge around in a morass of depressing thoughts. Winifred's task did not bode well. He wished there was a better solution.

The outline of the harbour entrance now defined itself through a curtain of drizzle, the place where the river Liffey merged with the sea. It would not be long before the queue started for disembarkation and so Pete tried to marshal his thoughts. He wondered if Winifred had made the whole thing up. He knew from Mike that she hated, as well as feared, his motor racing. She could grasp at any straw that offered her respite, might even tell a lie. He was in a no-win situation. Should he succeed at her bidding, the odds were that Mike would refuse to retire and be outraged that his best mate had been sent by his own mother to do her dirty work. Either way it would not end in an afternoon spent in the Guinness brewery sinking a glass of the brew out of the 10 million produced each day and then bunking off on a pub crawl. It would be back to England for him to face an embarrassing conversation with Winifred as well as a break-up with one of his two best mates. It might even lead Mike to suspect that his mon ami might have given in to his mother's plea because his chances of winning the world championship would be given a boost by his own withdrawal.

Sighing with melancholia he was about to go back inside when the boat's fog horn boomed, letting all on land know of its imminent arrival. It injected urgency into his search for some other way in which to solve his appalling dilemma. He felt a flash of anger at Mike for allowing his mother to be that upset. After all, should he not quit if he was causing her that degree of stress? Pete thought that if the roles were reversed he certainly would retire.

Pete leant on the boat railing, tightening the collar of the raincoat around his neck. He then did something that served him well on the grid before a race. He selected a point ahead on which to focus, the southern corner of the estuary. At the same time he began to control his breathing. Soon the mental fog began to clear and he found himself able to think more clearly. Okay, so Mike had a serious illness, one that should bar him from racing, so why was he stubbornly refusing to admit it? Was it possible that he was at the point where ceasing to race would not enhance or guarantee his good health in the future? In that case why not take that risk? It was, literally, a once in a lifetime opportunity, wasn't it, to become the first British world drivers' champion? At least he would go down in posterity, his name written in the sporting history books. Pete felt a rush of exhilaration at the notion of challenging the fates to do their worst.

But then his bubble was punctured as suddenly as it had begun. He wanted the world championship as much as Mike. He had given it Fangio out of charity once, so was it not his time? Did he not deserve it as much as Mike? The thought coincided with another blast from the boat's fog horn. It deflated his bubble. Hey, forget it. He had years left. Mike had none.

He stared morosely at a couple who stood on the sea wall, huddled under an umbrella while watching the boat approach. The fact of the matter, he thought, was all his conjecturing was useless as the probability was that if he failed to get Mike to quit racing then Winifred would simply inform the FIA and his championship chasing would end with the withdrawal of his international motor racing licence. In that event Mike would blame him as much as his mother. He spotted Duncan out on deck with Mike, joining the knot of people queuing for the exit. He had a flash of inspiration. What if he persuaded him to go on for just two more races, try to win them and thus gain enough points to remain ahead of Stirling by the end of the season, given the unreliability of his car? That option was positive and workable and Winifred would surely have to accept it. Surely she would not stand in the way of allowing him a short but clear run at the championship? And would not Mike benefit by finding himself less harassed and therefore be more likely to win those races?

He watched Duncan let out a hearty laugh and place an arm around Mike's shoulder as he told some story about him to the group of admirers, at which they all bellowed with laughter, Mike included.

What if Duncan knew of Mike's illness?

The notion hit Pete with some force. Duncan's friendship with Mike went back way beyond his first meeting with his mon ami mate. They had first come together at a pub bar during an argument, far less likely to produce a friendly relationship than being thrown together in a racing team. It was, indeed, highly likely that Duncan knew far more about Mike than anyone. He cursed himself for not having thought of it before. He had no alternative but to speak to Duncan first, to find out what he knew, tell him of Winifred's threat and confess his real motive in joining them on the short break. Pete thought about his own friendship with Mike, now under threat. The result of their days in Dublin might see it finished and that would hurt. Although the press portrayed them as joined at the hip, with the same temperament, a love of booze and hell raising, it was not accurate. They were friends undoubtedly, except that if he did get involved in Mike's outrageous escapades it was always to show his matiness. He was actually in some ways a loner, more sensitive and likely to suffer more pain at the ending of their friendship. With a heavy heart he joined Mike and Duncan in queuing for the exit.

\* \* \* \* \*

'You've known all along?'

'Most of the time, yeah,' Duncan said.

Pete tried to absorb it and waited some time to speak. They stood at the open entrance to The Turk's Head in Temple Bar, that part of Dublin that seemed to have as many pubs as drinkers. The air was fresher in the doorway, the inside reeking of tobacco smoke, the fog enveloping Mike as he stood at the counter smoking his pipe and surrounded by autograph hunters and eager onlookers.

Pete was hurt that Mike had taken Duncan into his confidence and not himself. Was he that mistrusted? And if so, why?

Duncan read his mind. 'It's not what you think, honestly Pete. He's scared that if he told you then Louise would find out and it could spread. He's scared of losing his racing licence, that's all it is.'

Pete opened his mouth wide in understanding. Of course. He now understood the reason for Mike's eccentric behaviour that had caused Louise and himself so much concern. He glanced at Mike grinning and joking with his fans.

'Yeah, I can see that. Yeah, poor bloke,' he said and blinked a little. A tiny ripple of the cheek muscles betrayed his emotion. He took a drink to cover up.

Duncan noticed it. 'Pete, before we talk to him why don't we wait till we get back? I'd like to bring Stuart in. We're too close to Mike. Stuart's a mate, yes, but he can stand back and think about things. He's a clever bugger, far brainier than us.' He gave a chuckle before taking a drink.

Pete was unsure. 'But that's spreading it if we bring Stuart in. Not what Mike wants, is it?'

Duncan sighed. 'I think it's coming to the boil Pete, I really do. What with these panic attacks and everything.' He hesitated. 'I'm with you on this. I've had years of it, talking to Winifred, helping her cope. Your idea of two races could do the job. Let's get Stuart in and the three of us talk about it, yeah?'

At that moment Mike happened to glance across at them. It was obvious they were talking about him, both in their expressions and body language and the occasional gesture towards where he stood. And then he was hit by a pain in the guts and half doubled up.

Duncan saw it happen. His sharp reaction caused Pete to turn round, in time to catch Mike's grimace of pain and his quick apology to the fans around him before moving quickly towards the rear of the pub.

Pete instinctively put down his glass and followed him, leaving Duncan uncertain.

He entered the toilet to find Mike putting a pill into his mouth and then bending down taking a mouthful of tap water with which to knock it back. Suddenly realising he was being watched, he turned his head to stare at Pete. The tension rose between them.

'Duncan told you?' He winced at another stab of pain.

'No, you clot, your mother.' Pete's little grin, his attempt to defuse the situation, was met by Mike wiping a hand across his mouth.

'Fuck's sake,' he said. 'She worries all the time. And it's nothing. All that happened was I lost one kidney. Now she's on about me going to lose the other.' He hesitated. 'I didn't tell you because, well…' He finished lamely.

'Yeah, I know, Duncan told me. You didn't want Louise to know. The FIA licence.'

'No, not just because of her, but…'

'She worries about you anyway. We all do.'

Mike wiped his hands on a towel. 'Great.' He looked at himself in the mirror. 'Simply great.'

'What, you mean you don't think we should worry? What do you expect us to do, just watch while you do this to yourself?'

'I'm not doing anything to myself. I'm in tip top condition. Perfectly fine.'

'But the doctors told you to stop. Isn't that what doctors are for, to tell you what to do?'

'Who told me to stop? What doctor?'

Pete hesitated a moment. 'Your mother told me. She's worried sick about you.'

Mike clasped both hands around the wash basin and lowered his head. 'Pete,' he said quietly, 'Just bugger off? Please mate?'

'Mike, she begged me to get you to quit.' Pete hesitated once more. 'She says the doctors asked her to get you to stop. If you don't she'll tell the FIA.'

Mike turned his head towards him, sighed, then looked once more at himself in the mirror. 'Yeah I know,' he said in tired fashion. 'Pete, can I ask you one more time, please, please, lay off? I've got this fucking stomach ache. Reflux. That's all it is.'

'No it's not. You know that. Come on.'

Mike put up a hand. 'Yeah, yeah, okay. I do have a problem. But mum's not telling the truth. She's not been told that by the quack because he told me I was okay for racing till the end of the season. Now, that's all it is, so bloody well stop worrying will you?'

'You're being stupid Mike. We want to help. Duncan says…'

'Pete.' Mike suddenly became angry. 'I know what I'm doing. And I'm not stupid!' He jabbed a finger towards Pete. 'I want to win this thing! What's the point, there's only five races left! I've been through all this with the consultant and then I get Duncan, I get my mother and now there's you. Then there'll be Louise!' He threw up his arms. 'For fuck's sake I'm just sick of it! I'm fine so just – why don't you all just leave me alone and do what you have to do instead of always…'

He broke off because there was no point. Pete had gone.

* * * * *

They came back to England the next morning, two days earlier than planned. The rain belt had moved away and the wet roads shone in the sunlight. The journey home was spent mostly in silence. Mike had not wanted another confrontation with Winifred and so accepted Duncan's offer to stay with him until the Wednesday following, 16 July. She would think he was still in Dublin and so there should be no worry on that score. As Duncan drove through the Cheshire countryside towards Stoke on Trent he became convinced that Stuart should be brought in. Pete, at first, had welcomed the idea, but had then thought more about it and wondered if, once briefed, Stuart might tell Stirling, his teammate, thus giving him a psychological boost in the championship stakes.

It was a risk that Duncan said he was prepared to take. That night he telephoned Stuart who admitted knowing that Mike had a kidney problem. 'Yeah, he told me. I said something about seeing a spot of blood in the loo.'

'Did he tell you how bad it was? That he had to have one of his kidneys removed?'

'No he didn't.'

After Stuart had heard the whole story, including the threat from Mike's mother to end his world championship bid, he took a deep breath. 'I think we all ought to meet. Don't you? Let's try and get something sorted? Sooner the better?'

'Precisely my idea Stuart.'

* * * * *

They met two days later at the Royal Automobile Club fronting Pall Mall in what was part of the old War Office. In a private lounge equipped with leather armchairs they were able to speak freely. Stuart said he had checked with The Federation International de l'Automobile, the governing body in Paris. They had informed him that they would never revoke a driver's licence without seeing the relevant medical certificate.

Pete's first reaction was relief, his debt to Winifred now irrelevant. His opinion was that once Mike knew that his licence was safe no amount of cajoling would extract him from his seat in a Ferrari until the season was over. Duncan agreed with him.

Pete said, 'I've just got to help him off the track as well as on…I know there's things I can do, get his mind sorted, make sure he gets some rest. In the race I've got to drive for him, pure and simple.'

Stuart looked a shade concerned. 'How do you mean you help him on the track Pete? You don't mean block Stirling?'

'Oh, no.' Pete laughed. 'I don't mean anything illegal. I'd stick with the rules.'

Stuart gave him a wry smile. 'Pete, you've already given away one world championship to Fangio. Don't tell me you're going to do it again?'

'I've got years left,' replied Pete. 'Mike's got five races, that's all. He won't have a chance next year. This is his last.' He paused. 'You know my idea that he might do just two more races? I don't think it will work. If he gets through them he'll go on. I know he will.'

Duncan said, 'Stuart's right Pete, how can you help him on the track? You mean by slowing down other drivers? You'd be disqualified.'

'How about *me* going faster?'

'Eh?' Duncan grinned. 'What do you mean?'

Pete grinned, enjoying the mystification he had caused. 'I've got an idea. But I'm not telling you because Stuart's here and it involves Stirling.'

'Stirling?' Stuart grimaced. 'What the blazes are you going to do?'

Pete was still grinning. 'I'm not telling you. I'll leave it as a surprise.'

The mood lightened at the teaser.

On the strength of it three more pints of 'Worthington E' were ordered. Duncan told an 'Irish joke' while they waited. After the laughter came the beers. They toasted Mike.

It became serious again when Stuart, who had been silent for a few moments, suddenly said, 'I disagree Pete about him not packing up after two more races. He could have enough points over Stirling. Out of three Vanwalls running we've had eight engine failures in only five races. It's amazing that Stirling's still up with a chance. Compare that with you and Ferrari. I worked out your failure rate is less than half of ours.'

Pete nodded. 'I still think he'll carry on.'

'Okay,' said Stuart. 'If he does he'll need counselling. He'll need somebody to…'

'He'll need what?' Duncan grinned at him.

'Counselling. It's a new thing. You talk to somebody to sort your mind out. Get a new fix on things. It's called psycotherapy. He needs somebody who can listen and…'

Duncan interrupted him. 'No way.'

'Why not?'

'No way. He won't see any kind of trick cyclist. No way. He'd run a mile.'

'It's not psychiatry,' replied Stuart. 'It's only 'talking'. If you don't want the professional I'll have a go. I'll talk to him.'

Duncan looked at Pete. 'Pete?'

Pete, who had been thinking, made a decisive gesture. 'I think what we can do realistically is try to make it as easy as we can for him. Be his gofer. Anything, whatever's needed. And when the time's right and he is really down then we should try to talk to him.'

Stuart grinned at Duncan. 'It's still psychotherapy. I know a therapist who'll do it much better than we…' He broke off in laughter as Duncan skimmed a small cushion at his head.

\* \* \* \* \*

Louise left New York in a BOAC de Havilland Comet on its overnight flight to London. She was worried. She had agreed to tour in the play *Romanoff and Juliet* directed by Peter Ustinov, who would also take a leading role. However, the dates she had been given would clash with at least one Grand Prix, she feared. Pete would know, as he had the dates. She had tried to speak to him by telephone but found that her calls were not answered in Monaco or at their home, Honeyford House in Worcestershire.

It put her in some anxiety as Pete always made sure there would be some answer to her transatlantic calls, either written in the form of a cable or telegram, or by a return phone call. It was in increasing concern that she decided to fly home a day earlier than planned.

Before she travelled to Heathrow she had given it her last shot by sending a request to Winifred by cable. Could she contact Pete in the hope that he had time to greet her at Heathrow the following morning?

Louise made the journey sitting in first class in a half recliner and wearing a dark eye patch, but found sleep difficult. She would remain in an anxious state until she saw Pete again. She need not have worried as, by chance, he had telephoned Winifred later that night to report that he had not yet managed to talk to Mike, but would do so 'very shortly'. Winifred was able to inform him of her morning arrival at Heathrow.

As Pete greeted her, after passing through Customs, she was quick to voice her concern. 'I'm scared Pete. I've got the rehearsal dates and I'm pretty sure one is the same weekend as the German Grand Prix. Can you look?'

As soon as they sat in the car Pete took out from his wallet a list of events. The German Grand Prix, as she feared, was fixed for 3 August. She had little chance of leaving the Nürburgring circuit on a Sunday evening and arriving fresh for rehearsal in New York the next morning, even if connecting flights were available.

'Pete, I just can't let you go round that track, 15 mile circuits, without me being there.'

'Fourteen point one miles actually,' smiled Pete. 'Don't worry, I'll be fine.'

'You might be, but I won't. I hate the Nürburgring. Last year was terrible, waiting to see you come round each lap, but I have to be there because then I know you'll be okay. You won't have any…' She broke off, sat upright and blew her nose in a handkerchief.

'Sweetheart?' He put a hand on her neck.

She looked at him.

'There'll be no shunts with me around,' Pete promised. 'I am the safest driver, ask anybody. I drive every second like there's going to be an accident and I sort it out. I'm no lunatic driver. Luigi killed himself because he was driving like a madman. But he had a reason. Don't worry. I'm going to stay in once piece. You can shoot me if I don't.'

She smiled a little. Pete switched on the car radio and they drove off to Perry Como singing one of the hit songs of the year, *Catch a Falling Star*. They arrived at Honeyford House at midday.

Despite her weariness Louise demanded that Pete send a telegram to Peter Ustinov asking if she could have the weekend of 3 August free from rehearsal. Pete did as she requested, told her it was done and reassured, she fell asleep almost immediately.

Surprisingly, when she woke up at 6pm Pete had already received Ustinov's reply, which read: 'Of course. But make sure you learn the lines. Or else. Love Peter.'

She laughed and told Pete to open a bottle. They could celebrate.

Pete allowed her to enjoy the evening meal, which he had cooked. Afterwards they went for a short walk around the two acre garden. They had reached the fountain that Pete had himself built when he gave her the news about Mike.

There was a long silence with Louise staring at him in shock, then a hand came quickly to her mouth. 'That's awful, Pete. I didn't know…'

'He's okay. He'll get through the rest of the races.'

'But how can he be okay?' She put her hand to her chest. 'I didn't know. Oh, that's awful. Poor Mike.'

Later, it being a cool evening, Pete lit a fire and they sat in front of the flames, both lost in their own thoughts. Louise finally spoke. 'I knew something was wrong when he dashed home, do you remember? We were on *Mipooka* and he suddenly had to go back to Farnham, about the garage business or something? Before the French race? He had just done the Monza 500. He seemed to go down after that. Did you notice?'

She rested her head on Pete's shoulder. 'And I've seen him taking a pill when he thought nobody was looking.' She sat upright and took a deep breath. 'It's obvious nobody will make him change his mind. If he is really ill it means he's gone through this year's races absolutely determined. I mean he must have suffered so he's not going to pack up now, is he, with only five races left? It would mean none of the pain would have been worth it.'

Pete looked at her impressed. 'That's exactly what he says.'

'I bet he does. He'll be completely destroyed if he quits and finds that he could have gone on, after all.' She laid her head back again on Pete's shoulder. 'It's awful. Poor Mike.' She put a hand to an eye and wiped away a tear, then suddenly leaned forward to stare into the fire.

'Look,' she said deliberately. 'Mike's a dear friend, but friendship depends on trust. He won't trust us again if we show we're badgering him, will he? He'll be on a knife edge and so will we, and we'll all feel worse. So why not do the opposite? Instead of trying to put him off, why not encourage him? Let him go for it. And you do what you have to do to help him. He'll be grateful and feel better about himself. Does it make sense?'

'Yeah, it does. I'm going to try and see Mike tomorrow. I've got to make sure no more upsets. Practice starts the day after.'

* * * * *

Duncan had made breakfast when the telephone rang in the oak panelled hallway. He went to answer it. 'Hullo Pete. You okay? Yeah, I'll get him, hold on.' He went back to the dining room to speak to Mike. 'It's Pete, for you.'

Mike walked into the hallway and picked up the receiver. 'How's it going mon ami?' He was keen to dissipate the tension following the bust up in Dublin.

'I'm fine mate. How are you today?'

'Could not be better. Duncan's taking me out for a round at Wentworth.'

'Oh.' Pete sounded a little disappointed, but recovered quickly. 'I was just going to come over, you know, and have a chin wag. Sorry I barged out on you in Dublin. I shouldn't have done that.'

'Done what? What are you talking about? Where's Dublin?'

Pete was immensely relieved. 'Thanks. I just wanted you to know that nobody's going to bug you any more. We're right behind you.'

He hesitated, unsure Mike would like his next statement. 'Stuart said you'd told him about your problem and he's on board as well. So no problems.'

'On board what? Not that bloody ferry again! I was almost sick coming back!'

Pete sighed in relief. 'Great, it's been difficult. But there's three of us – and Louise – we're right behind you mate. But you do what you have to.'

'Thanks. Stuart rang me 10 minutes ago. Sorry I sounded off at you. But it's been bit of a pig. It gets you.'

'Of course it does! Look. Anybody would, I mean, if you're not feeling well. Did Duncan tell you about your mother and the FIA? They won't revoke your licence without you giving permission?'

'He did. I feel tons better already.'

'Great. Okay, so have a good round and don't stay too long in the 19th. It's first practice the day after tomorrow, don't forget.'

'How can I? And this time don't let your air scoop get stuck in your knickers!'

They said goodbye in laughter.

Mike came back into the dining room. 'Duncan I need to get home.'

He said he had to see Winifred but did not want to go alone as he needed back-up. This was one bit of guilt that he could get rid of, but it might get out of hand and he was not good at the emotional stuff. But somehow he needed to make it right with her. He was going to admit that he had treated her badly. She had lied about the request from the consultant, now he intended to lie, in fact swear blind that he had been to the hospital with Duncan and that the consultant had cleared him for the last five races.

On their arrival Winifred was not in the house. Mike was still searching when Duncan called him into the kitchen and indicated that he should look through the window.

Mike looked. There she sat in a deck chair between two apple trees, a cup of tea in her hand and staring blankly at the ground in front of her. A picture of loneliness.

He thought about it and then asked Duncan if he would not mind leaving him there and returning home. He said he would stay there overnight and drive back to Duncan's the next morning for their journey to Silverstone. It would give him time to make it up with his mum, he said.

Duncan understood and wished him the best of luck. After he had driven away Mike went into the garden. Winifred saw him and her eyes lit up. He crouched down beside her and gave her a hug. She burst into tears.

'It's all okay mum. Everything's going to be fine. I've got some great news.' He held her close and stroked her hair.

* * * * *

### Silverstone Race Circuit, 19 July 1958

Britain was the only country to stage a Grand Prix on a Saturday. The Christian church in all its denominations as well as the majority of the public, insisted that Sunday was not suitable for noisy and dangerous entertainment. They were led in this by The Lords Day Observance Society who pledged to keep the Sabbath as God had ordered, a day of rest. In an age when many of the working class, as well as the upper classes, would not even go to the cinema on a Sunday it was generally looked upon as only right and proper.

In anticipation of the duel between Mike Hawthorn and Stirling Moss, it was the largest crowd ever to attend a motor race in Britain on a circuit that still bore the look of a World War Two bomber airfield, especially in the crossing of two runways at its centre. A sign at each entrance warned that 'Motor racing is dangerous' and spectators were 'admitted at their own risk'.

Apart from the privileged few in the grandstand most of the huge crowd stood close to the track from which they were separated by a single rope. As a token concession to safety, earth banks gave the spectators a mere 5ft of elevation above the action. There were no run-off areas and no escape roads for cars that spun off or crashed. Catch fencing had not yet been invented. Should a car leave the track it was likely that some spectators would be killed or injured. In another concession to safety, straw bales had been stacked at the apexes of the corners and for some way beyond. These, the product of surrounding farmland, were there to act as impact absorbers should there be an accident, but gave scant protection for the people who stood behind them.

As if all this were too 'sissy' for some spectators a ritual would take place just before the start of the race by which they would demonstrate their bravado. Adults as well as children, would slip under the rope and go down the bank to crouch behind the straw bales. They would wait for the race to start and then stick out their heads to watch the pack of racing cars hurtle towards them. Then they would close their eyes ready for the fierce blast of dust and grit to strike their faces as they roared past. Having had their thrill they would then retire to the earth banking from where they would watch the rest of the race.

Many spectators, mostly young men, found their excitement in the anticipation of an accident. There was usually some coming together of cars on the track, some shunt or other. Their keen air of expectancy would have been felt by the citizens of Rome attending the ancient Games, albeit with a greater intensity. The spectacle of death in the afternoon, for them was a certainty. At Silverstone, on this grey summer's day, it was a distinct possibility. Death or injury was not sought by these young men, of course not. What they sought was the sensation of schadenfreude felt by witnessing a crash quickly followed by sudden relief at realising that no one had been killed or injured. It was a thrill upmarket of any that a rollercoaster could provide.

* * * * *

For Louise, alone with Pete in the motor home, it was pure fear that she experienced and which would not be alleviated until the race was over. To help combat the stress she acted as the general factotum. Making tea and fussing about kept her busy and controlled her nerves.

'I've got a plan.' Pete stuck the last piece of transparent plastic across his visor. He said it with such deliberation that Louise turned to look at him.

'I'm going to blast off. I'm going to give it the gun right from the go. Stirling's engine is dodgy. If he sees me belt off he'll give it the hammer. He'll chase me, I know he will. I just know it.'

'And what will that do Pete?' Louise looked at him in all innocence.

'With any luck he'll blow up. His engine I mean.'

'But – why?'

Pete stood up and gave her a hug. 'Sweetie, if Stirling drops out…?' He raised her eyebrows at her leaving the rest implied. 'Get it?'

'Oh you mean that would give Mike a better chance?'

'That's it. You are gorgeous. You know that?' He kissed her.

She leaned back from the kiss. 'But what if your engine blows up doing it?'

'Tough.'

'Have you told Mike?'

Pete hesitated and she knew he had. 'Yes,' he said. 'He said he wanted to win it on his own. Well, he would, wouldn't he?'

'Did he say anything else?'

'No He tried to strangle me.'

'That's good,' Louise said with a smile. 'That's the old Mike.'

Suddenly it hit her, the sacrifice that he was making. It made her angry. She wanted to say how terrible it was that she suffered for as long as Pete stayed on the track and what was the point of it all if he was going to risk his life just to support another driver, even though it was Mike? Not only that but did it not put off Pete's attempt at winning the world crown? She could not wait for the season to end. It was her second year of being frightened and she didn't want it to go into a third. Louise had a much better and safer plan for Pete and it had nothing to do with motor racing. If he won the championship – and how she yearned for that despite her concern for Mike – then she would try to persuade him to quit and return with her to live in America where she would introduce him to her world of entertainment. Were not the press always talking about his stunningly charismatic image and was it not often remarked upon by their friends that, as a couple, they produced the same kind of star appeal akin to that of Humphrey Bogart and Lauren Bacall? Was not Pete's tremendous charm and Louise's sensuous aura just made for film? Did they not have that same electricity that audiences experienced when watching Clark Gable and Carole Lombard, or Richard Burton and Elizabeth Taylor? After all, Pete was a good actor. In the numerous antics that he and Mike got up to he was the one who could impersonate almost anybody and in so doing create great hilarity.

Above all, she knew, his sincerity would shine through. He would be Britain's answer to Douglas Fairbanks, the handsome star of the old swashbuckling films, but better looking. And if anyone suggested she was looking through rose tinted spectacles she would retort that the best actors were not always trained. She, herself, had been a model who had been overheard talking to someone by a producer who was auditioning actors for the road company of the play *Mr Roberts*. He had told her that her voice was magical and wanted to give her a screen test. The rest was history.

In the event that this brave plan would not work out she had a fall back situation. Her father, Andrew Cordier, was Executive Assistant to Trygve Lie, the first Secretary General of the United Nations. That was a big contact. Not just big, very big.

And there was no doubting that Pete was charming, intelligent and diplomatic. It would be a big string to pull, but worth it. She was certain that a post could be found for him having talked to her father about it.

But, she said nothing of this to Pete. She would not dream of messing up his mind with such stuff, especially before a race. He needed all his concentration to stay safe. How she wished that he was getting ready to go to a sound stage or the office rather than prepare himself for yet another terrifying ordeal, but hers not his. The awful irony was that he was confident as ever, calm, serene even. He even enjoyed it.

As she watched him don his white overalls she prayed for his safety. Their marriage was not one built on sand, as some had predicted following their whiz-bang one week meeting and marriage. She had been married before, at the age of 18, to actor John Michael King – and yes – that had been a mistake. But in marrying Pete so quickly after their first meeting it was not on physical attraction alone. There had been an instant recognition that they were meant for each other. She loved him beyond anything, even to distraction. She closed her eyes. If anything should happen to him…

\* \* \* \* \*

Mike spent the last few minutes chatting with Tavoni about his car's understeer, its habit of going wider round corners than he intended. He thought that being placed fourth on the grid had been caused by that tendency during practice. After the last session he had told Tavoni that if the set-up of his car could be 'tweaked' without incurring a 'domino effect' – the knock-on process in which other parts of the set-up are affected in turn – he would go for it. But Tavoni could not give him that reassurance. It could take days to sort out if the first tweak did not work. Mike had accepted his opinion. He was not that disappointed to be fourth on the grid as the front row at Silverstone could take four cars abreast. He would be sitting on the outside, with Harry Schell and Roy Salvadori on his inside. The bad news, ominously, was that Stirling Moss was 'on pole', giving him a shorter run to the first corner.

A ripple of excitement ran through the grandstand as the first cars were being pushed out of the garages on to the track. But there were still empty seats dotted around. Even as the grid started to fill there were still people stuck in traffic jams on the country roads leading to this small part of rural Northamptonshire. Their frustration was made worse knowing that the two most popular English stars of motor racing would start head to head in 15 minutes time. Throughout the country people were tuning in their wireless sets ready for the race commentary to begin.

Pete came out of the motor home with Mike. Taffy was already in the pits. The three shook hands as per custom and walked out onto the grid. After seating himself in the car Mike glanced towards his garage. He could see Louise sitting on the pit counter with her lap board and stop watch at the ready.

Then he looked at the initial '10 Minute Board' held up by the race steward standing a few yards in front of him. The countdown to the warm up lap had begun.

At this point Mike switched all his attention to the car. After the engine had fired he noted the initial oil pressure reading. He would monitor that instrument throughout the race. Other checks were okay. He controlled his breathing in the manner Stuart had suggested by which he might prevent another panic attack. Breathing and focus. He stared ahead towards the corner, hoping to beat Stirling to it but, failing that, to get there ahead of the other two front runners, Harry Schell and Roy Salvadori. His plan was to attack the curve on an acute line of entry. It meant crossing the track ahead of Harry and Roy but he thought he was capable.

It would require a precision launch. He would need to execute a perfect synchronisation of throttle and clutch to that end.

After the warm up lap Mike's car was the last to settle itself on the front row. With the grandstand resounding to the thunder of 20 formula one engines he half turned to give Pete, on the second row, his usual 'thumbs up'. As he did so he caught sight of someone else sitting on the Ferrari pits counter, apart from Louise. It was a woman dressed in black. It was Carlotta. And she was staring at him. What was she doing there! Forget her. He tore his eyes away and started talking to himself in the calm manner of his father after he had taken possession of his first performance car, a Riley Sprite.

'Push clutch down. Press throttle. Keep revs in the middle range. Lift foot from the clutch slowly. Car about to move. Keep both pedals steady.'

Was it a dream? It was not. She was still there. Flag's up.

'Slowly up with clutch. And hold. Press throttle. And hold…hold.'

His breathing was all over the place. The image was fixed in his mind. An avenging angel. Flag down. Launch. Too many revs. Big tyre spin. Burning rubber.

Fuck it.

# **Chapter** Seven

The Pathe newsreel Voice Over by John Parsons summed up the race in his usual vigorous and upbeat tone:

'Mike Hawthorn made a slow start at Silverstone this weekend. It was Stirling Moss, his rival for the world championship, who took the lead in front of their home crowd. Both men are equal favourites to win the world drivers' championship. But it was another Englishman who stirred the cockles of British hearts. Peter Collins overtook Stirling after a few laps and never looked back. Mike had to be content with second place. He wasn't pleased. He didn't get his customary beer. "Leave some for me mate!" complains Mike!'

The voice-over ends with amusing film of a thirsty looking Mike watching Pete in envy as he drains a pint of bitter. Camera pulls back to show Pete walking to the trestle table to collect his large silver cup from Max Aitken of the *Daily Express*. With the sleeves of his light blue cotton overalls rolled up, he holds it aloft with a dazzling smile for the crowd in the grandstand first, and then the photographers. The grandstand explodes with ovations. Mike hugs him.

The previous year the winners and runner-up had also been British, Stirling Moss and Tony Brooks. With another two Brits taking their places the enthusiasm for motor racing in Great Britain had reached record proportions. The fans were stunned and delighted by the margin of Pete's win over Mike, having crossed the finish line approximately 24 seconds ahead.

The Golden Boy himself, not minding a jot that his best mate had given him a thrashing but mystified that it had not been his avowed intention, collared him once they were in the paddock. He imitated a slow Oliver Hardy-like grimace at the dim witted antics of a bemused Stan Laurel, speaking to him in the same long suffering patient tone of voice.

'You told me you were going to help me win the race. How did you expect me to catch up with you 24 point two seconds ahead?'

Pete adopted Stanley's look of mild denseness. 'I could not slow down to let you catch up by 24 seconds could I? The fans would not have liked it, would they?'

Ironically, he had been too successful. Yes, he had accomplished his main aim of forcing Stirling out of the traps to chase him 'balls out' from the start. The Vanwall engine had, indeed, blown up halfway through the race unable to take the pressure, but by that time Pete was already so far ahead of Mike that short of deliberately blowing up his own engine he had been forced to accept victory as the price of failure. If he had allowed Mike to overtake him with an advantage of 24 seconds it would have gone down as a gross betrayal of sportsmanship. Instead of the grandstand bursting with cheers it would have been jeers. The fans would have watched a meaningless race in terms of championship points won or lost.

'So you see mate, I'm as pissed off as you are,' said Pete.

'What for?'

'Because I beat you.'

'So what?' Mike was still Oliver Hardy, speaking slowly and pedantically. 'Pete, I came second. I only lost one point from being the winner. I am now seven points clear of Stirling, so why should you be sorry? And you got eight points.'

'I know but...'

'I moved up seven points, Stirling didn't win any points.'

'I know that but...'

'Simple arithmetic. We both won! Now stop being a sentimental bugger! Grrr!' Mike put both hands around Pete's throat and strangled him.

The play acting over, Pete asked Mike if he knew why Carlotta had turned up. 'You'd have thought a race track was the last place she'd want to come to.'

Mike did not want to own up to her disrupting his race launch. 'Yeah, I'll talk to Tav about it.' On pain of death he ordered Pete not to repeat his 'blow up Stirling' ploy on their next outing in Germany. 'I want to win this thing on my own mate. So no more fucking charity!'

Pete was mollified, having worried that Mike may not have believed his story of being forced to win the race. Now he was free to enjoy his memory of it. He summed it all up in a radio interview: 'I was out there on my own. It was like, I dunno, the nearest thing to a driver's heaven I suppose.'

Louise, for her part, could be said to have had 'a good race'. At least her suffering had been suspended during the long period that Pete had spent away from 'the ragged edge' of competition, the constant dancing between disaster and safety. Out in front of the pack he had been in much less danger than when jockeying for position surrounded by other cars. And if he could maintain his charge and win the championship he would, she hoped, be the more easily persuaded to retire. In that vein of optimism she wrote to her parents back home:

'It was a really good and happy race. We were thrilled by the whole thing. I wish every race was like that. The fans went wild. We're so happy. Can we carry on being the luckiest people in the world?'

Further adding to her pleasure was having seen Mike strangle the giggling Pete. He had not shown the slightest trace of jealousy or resentment towards him. Considering how much winning the world championship meant to him it spoke volumes about Mike's magnanimity. She recalled a remark that he had made to Pete, something that proved their friendship had real depth:

'You're a bloody oaf. But if you'd been a woman I'd have married you.'

＊ ＊ ＊ ＊ ＊

No one was happier than Romolo Tavoni. Not only had he seen two of his three cars take first and second places but Pete's win dismissed any suspicion that it was Mike who was Enzo's favoured driver.

Enzo celebrated in Maranello by lighting his favourite cigar. He was at his pomp, like a Roman emperor hearing of a triumphant victory led by one of his generals. He gave thanks to God that no one had been killed or injured. He was optimistic that his overwhelming success in England would silence his detractors, not least the church. Nevertheless, he made a note to himself that he telephone Archbishop Urbani of Verona with the good news. This high ranking priest was one of the few who had supported his work in the glorification of his country. He also jotted down a note reminding him to pay Tavoni his bonus on time at the end of the month. He thought he might pitch in another thousand lire for good luck.

The victory had another, personal, effect upon Enzo. Every Ferrari win acted upon him like an aphrodisiac. With his loins stirred – and despite his decision to wait awhile – he could not help himself but pen a love letter to Carlotta, hoping that she would be able to visit him between races.

The party in the paddock that night featured the usual bonfire in which potatoes were baked and meat barbecued. The beer came in bottles. Many of the wives and girlfriends were content with the newly marketed and feminised 'Babycham' that had recently been prominent in television advertising. But whatever their sex, they were all friends, rivalries on the track forgotten in the camaraderie of the evening. And, because it was on British soil, Stirling stayed later than usual.

Mike sat in the inner circle around the bonfire with Pete and Louise, Harry Schell, Stuart and Duncan. Harry, who in the race had come a creditable fourth in his BRM, livened proceedings by singing the American ballad, *The Death of John Henry* to the accompaniment of someone playing the harmonica. It was met with a whooping and a hollering.

A number of toasts were awarded Pete for his fabulous win. Every one of the 20 drivers that day had now congratulated him. Stirling had been the first after Mike to praise his opponent. 'Pete, that was a great drive,' he said. Then, having rejoined Tony Vandervell, the owner of the Vanwall team, he confessed that his chances of winning the world championship were 'now small'. Nevertheless, he would 'give it his best shot'.

Carlotta stood in the outer circle around the bonfire opposite Mike's group. Next to her stood her 'tame' mechanic enjoying her present of a beer. Her seemingly innocent questions were put to him in her role as Enzo's spy. It irked that Collins had won the race but it was more than compensated for by her growing sense of power over Hawthorn. She had no doubt that her stare had upset him at the start and caused him to lose the race. As the evening wore on she was pleased to see that he remained at the fireside, looking glum. Usually by that time he would have been absent from the bonfire on the hunt for a woman.

On the other hand Pete, Duncan and Stuart, thought it was purely Mike's preoccupation with his illness that kept him quiet. Harry Schell tried to joke him out of his mood, in ignorance of its cause. It was down to Mike button-holing Tavoni as soon as he had finished the routine work of loading the team transporters. He had drawn him aside to put the question: 'What was Carlotta doing in the pits when you know she hates me? She hid herself until the start, then she's suddenly there on the pit counter and staring at me like a bloody vulture.'

Tavoni had shrugged and shaken his head. 'Mike. Yes. You are right. She should not be here. But Enzo put her with us, so what can I do?'

'Yeah, but why is she here? What's Enzo up to?'

Tavoni paused. 'He thinks she will be better for herself because of losing Luigi. It will make it quicker. Her mourning.' He flinched a little at Mike's stare. 'Well…'

Mike shook his head in utter disbelief. 'Well, I want her gone. It's crazy. Can you tell Enzo or do I have to?'

'No Mike. Let me talk to her. I will sort it out tonight, don't worry.'

In the event Tavoni did not talk to Carlotta, wary of what might happen, given her unpredictability. As to the real motive behind Enzo allowing her into the pits he could only surmise. Having been his personal secretary Tavoni was well aware of the sexual drive that both paralleled and intertwined with his business life; he knew full well that he would never have asked Carlotta to travel all that distance to Maranello in order to help her grieve efficiently. He could have made the suggestion by telephone. He must have known that he was taking a risk in placing her in the vicinity of Mike and Pete. By keeping her close, in Tavoni's view, it demonstrated how much he wanted her that he was willing to take that risk. Tavoni saw Enzo as a fisherman placing his catch into a net, which he then submerged, ready to take out when it suited him. He regretted not telling Enzo about the garden incident at Reims when Carlotta had screamed out in condemnation of the two Englishmen. Others knew about it – news travels fast in motor racing circles – but, of course, no one would have dared bypass Tavoni to inform Enzo.

As the party carried on – and with Carlotta not showing any aggression or move to upset anyone – Tavoni was thankful, deciding to bury his concern and resign himself to developments. However, for the next race, the German Grand Prix, he reminded himself to keep a careful watch on her movements. If she did create a problem for Mike or Pete he would then have no alternative but to inform Enzo and hope that he could manage her in some 'other capacity'.

Stirling's conversation with Tony Vandervell had been overheard and soon the news reached Tavoni who immediately whispered it to Pete who then transmitted it to Mike.

'Tav says that Stirling's given up. He told Tony he can't win the championship, so stop bloody moping and think about Germany. You're going to win there, I know you are.'

Mike nodded, trying to look pleased but still unable to take his eyes off Carlotta's face shimmering opposite in the rising heat from the fire.

Carlotta's mechanic had now disappeared to be replaced by a tall, slim middle-aged woman who wore jewellery on both hands. A yellow cardigan was draped over her shoulders. Mike feared that the slight turns of her head as she talked to Carlotta were in his direction, suggesting that he was the subject of their conversation.

Mike had gone through trauma the likes of which only battlefield soldiers usually experience. His feelings of being persecuted had not started at Reims, but at Le Mans in 1955. He still remained troubled by the disaster. Added to that was Luigi's death, at whose funeral Carlotta had offered him her dead candle. He could not rid himself of the memory of that veiled face, the dark thin smile playing at the corners of her lips, the hard glint in her eyes. She was a real and genuine threat, by no means the product of his imagination.

He asked questions of himself. 'Wasn't it unbelievable that he should suffer like this? Where was natural justice and fairness? How could he be offered the world and be denied it at the same time?'

From the public point of view he was still The Golden Boy, standing on a pedestal like a classical hero, bursting with vigorous energy, one on whom the sun permanently shone, invulnerable to any kind of harm. But then, in direct contrast, was the hunted man singled out by the malevolent fates. In such a dichotomy the weak self would always undermine the strong.

'Why me?' was the question that ignited a feeling that his intolerable burden of guilt could not be born much longer. Whatever, answers were needed.

The woman talking to Carlotta cast a glance towards him. It brought a hot flush to his hands and face, now convinced that they were talking about him.

After the last party guests had drifted away, Mike discovered via Duncan that the woman in question was Elvira Massingham, a rich divorcee from Boston, Massachusetts, and had come to Silverstone as a guest of the elegant ex-Guards officer, Raymond Mays, the founder of the BRM motor racing team.

Mike then heard from Harry Schell that she had talked to him earlier that evening about his connections with American motor racing that went back to 1940 when he had run two cars in the Indianapolis 500 race. She had told him of her interest in numerology and had discovered that many sportsmen, especially racing drivers, were susceptible to superstition. Initially she had explored the lives and performances of drivers carrying numbers on their cars in American racing. This had proved promising and had prompted her to widen her study to include the world of Grand Prix. It was Sam Hanks, winner of the 1957 Indy 500 race, who had introduced her to Raymond Mays via a mutual contact.

Luigi Musso's death especially interested her because he had the number 22 allocated to his car at Reims. For Elvira it was a powerful number as evidenced by The Hebrew alphabet having 22 letters. Also The Revelation of John in the bible had 22 chapters.

Similarly, in the Kabbalah there were 22 paths within the sephiroth. This was backed up anecdotally, 22 being generally regarded as a lucky number.

However, she had come across some anomalies that were worth exploring. In each case the individual concerned reported that they 'felt themselves living in two worlds', one that was overwhelmed by the mundane and the other by the fantastic. Armed with this information she had then turned to researching their background, finding that the number 22 brought luck and success to those who did not misuse it. But, ominously, for those who tried to use it deliberately as a lucky omen it had often led to some kind of disaster or 'a wasted life'.

Harry had learnt that Elvira had come to Silverstone having been told that Luigi's friend, Carlotta, would be there and was anxious to talk to her. Fortunately Elvira was an Italian speaker and had the insight and sensitivity to cease talking with Carlotta about those things that might upset her. She was pleasantly surprised, therefore, to find that far from rejecting her, Carlotta was a ready and interested listener. Far from giving Elvira short shrift she actually encouraged her into an open discussion. On being asked if she knew of any disturbances in Luigi's life on the day he died Carlotta had answered with an adamant 'Si'. Yes, Luigi was determined to win the race, she said. He had to win the race, else he would have been murdered.

Elvira, shaken by the statement, thanked her, wished her well and was leaving to rejoin Raymond Mays when Carlotta stopped her to ask one last question. She wondered if the number 22, carried by someone who knew that it made them vulnerable, might also meet the same fate as Luigi?

'Si, potrebbe avere lo stesso effeto,' said Elvira, agreeing that anyone with that number and with a heightened sense of the existence of 'hidden enemies' could also suffer from the same effect.

The evening ended with Mike being appalled by what Harry had told him. He was not to know it but the number 22 would soon have a very powerful effect upon the fate of one of the mon ami mates.

\* \* \* \* \*

Pete and Louise had expected Mike to return to Monaco with them ahead of the German Grand Prix in two weeks' time. He made his apologies to them both and then confided in Pete that he had a hospital appointment that had to be kept. There would be no problem, it being a routine check, he declared. He said he would rejoin them a day or two later.

Mike sat in the consultancy office in Guy's Hospital staring at a wall calendar opened at July and featuring a beautiful girl basking on a Caribbean beach.

'Well.' The consultant came into the room, sat down, propped both arms up on the desk by the elbows and looked Mike straight in the eye.

'I told you that I could find no direct evidence that the right kidney had been affected. I have now. It's showing signs. I can't swear that motor racing is responsible but why take the risk? It's in your best interests to stop. I mean stop absolutely. Now.'

Mike paused then nodded.

The consultant spread out his hands. 'It's up to you. I can do no more.'

Mike went home and sat in the living room. Winifred was out shopping. Grogger came in and sat by his side. He fondled his ears while pondering on his misfortune. Finding no relief he went into the hallway and picked up the dog's lead hanging from the side of the umbrella stand. The walk with the dog took him past houses and gardens that were quiet and still. It had started to rain a little.

On arriving home he found that Winifred had just returned with a bag of shopping. He helped her unpack, told her that he was fine, that the consultant had said his condition was stable. She bravely tried to accept it, had no wish to upset Mike further. But then she simply could not help herself. She just had to be certain, had to find rest for her mind. She tried to put it gently. 'Had the consultant said anything specific?'

Then, without the complete reassurance she so badly needed, she delicately began to rephrase the question. Soon the questions multiplied and still she had no satisfactory answer from a prevaricating Mike. His repeated requests for her to leave him alone served only to heighten her anxiety and finally led to an accusation that he was lying.

In more sorrow than anger, tired and dispirited and needing to escape, he rang Duncan. Could he meet him at The Barley Mow? He would only have a pint, no harm done.

He stepped out of the house with only one thought on his mind – escape. His highly tuned Jaguar 3.4 saloon painted in British Racing Green stood on the driveway. Unlike Enzo, who found that sitting in one of his creations was an erotic, stimulating sensation, Mike always found relaxation. He enjoyed the smell of the leather and the rumble of the engine on start up. Later, when the day was clear and the road appropriate he might slip into racing mode and let it all hang out. But not today.

He went to open the front gates and then returned to the car. He fired the engine, selected reverse gear, then let in the clutch. As the car moved backwards he had forgotten about Grogger. The dog wandered into its path, was knocked down by a rear wheel, then crushed as the car ran over it, its body lying stuck between the underside of the car and the concrete driveway.

Frozen in horror, he finally leapt out of the car to see two trickles of blood envelop the base of the rear wheel and meet in a small pool. Letting out an anguished cry he sank to the ground on both knees, sobbing.

Winifred, rushed out of the house and screamed at what she saw. Ten minutes later the family GP arrived to give her a sedative. It was arranged for the vet's assistant to come round to take away the dog's body, a task that was beyond Mike who rang Duncan and in a shaky voice cancelled their meeting. He spent the rest of the afternoon sitting on a sofa in the lounge staring at the empty fireplace.

There was only one conclusion to be drawn from it. The things that he loved most were being taken away as punishment. The issue was clear: how could he struggle on with so much against him? He decided to fly to Monaco as soon as he could, to be with Pete and Louise whose *joie de vivre* would prove comforting.

At 6pm, just as he had finished packing his case, the telephone rang in the hallway. It was Pete. Mike was about to tell him that he was on his way when Pete interrupted to say that Louise had seen Carlotta sitting on the harbour wall not far from *Mipooka*. She had walked towards her, hoping to invite her on board for a drink, get to know her and somehow defuse her antipathy towards them. But Carlotta had spotted her, stood up and walked hurriedly away.

Pete had no idea of the fear that his news generated in Mike since he had told them nothing about the effect that she had on him at the race launch at Silverstone.

'What's she doing in Monaco?' Mike's voice sounded a trifle shaky.

'No idea mate.' Pete wondered if she might be there as a guest of one of the racing drivers who were domiciled in the Principality.

Mike decided that he would be safer, until he sorted things out, staying at home.

\* \* \* \* \*

Carlotta sat outside the main restaurant in Casino Square, drinking a cocktail and re-reading Enzo Ferrari's second letter of the week. It was couched in the most romantic of terminology and made her smile. She had not replied so far because she enjoyed the thought of letting him sweat awhile, something in the way of revenge for the way he had treated Luigi and fawned over Collins. While she was thinking about it another idea struck her. When the moment came for her to be seduced why not suggest to him that she be commissioned to write road test reports on Ferrari sports cars, specialising in the female point of view? And when he was coming to a climax why not ask if she might borrow a 250 GT for six months. 'Yes…yes,' he would pant. Good, now what about a year's loan?

With a smug smile she stuffed the letter back in her handbag and turned her thoughts back to the Englishmen. Collins was no longer in her targeting sights, having heard via her tame mechanic that he had tried to persuade

Hawthorn to allow Luigi to share their prize money. In a way it suited her. Far better to devote all her energies towards the downfall of Hawthorn. It had worked so far. She thought ahead to the German Grand Prix in a week's time and imagined herself standing at the track side on one of the lonely stretches that ran through the forest. Then, when Hawthorn's car appeared she would hurl a brick at him. She saw his car spinning and sliding, then overturning and his body smashing into the ground. Her features set in sombre reflection. Immediately after Luigi's death she would have willingly thrown *herself* at his car.

She came out of her dark reverie. Maybe her revenge might not be needed. She had learnt that the average death rate at the 'Ring' per year was six. In one year recently it had risen as high as 12. It gave hope.

Pete and Louise flew from Nice to Cologne on the Thursday before the race and met Harry Schell who, as usual, was in bullish good humour. From the airport the trio drove to the racetrack where the Sporthotel occupied part of the grandstand opposite the pits, the drivers' favourite base since it cut out all the hassle of driving to the circuit each day. Mike was already booked in, having arrived with Duncan the previous evening. Both of them stood in the morning sunlight watching the Scuderia Ferrari transporters roll into the paddock with a total of five racing cars, one being a Dino 156 for Phil Hill to drive, a Formula Two car that the race organisers had allowed to compete along with the full complement of F1 cars in the Grand Prix.

Mike decided that he would use his early appearance at the circuit to get in some unofficial practice laps. He was joined on the track by teammate Taffy.

Stirling, the eternal early bird, had already been out on the circuit, regretting having been overheard at Silverstone lamenting his diminished chances of winning the world championship and so had arrived two days earlier than planned, determined to make amends. His first session had been spent working out his braking points as well as the lay out of the corners. This time he intended that his driving did the talking.

It spoke volumes. On the Friday's official practice session he beat Mike's time by two seconds.

This appeared to harden Mike's resolve. His friends observed his demeanour and were quietly pleased. There was no angst, no sense of crisis this time and he gave himself every encouragement the next day by smashing Fangio's breathtaking circuit record by 3.4 seconds. It put him on pole position.

Mike's performance was the talk of the packed bar that Saturday night. But the man himself shunned the limelight and spent some time making enquiries about Elvira Massingham. He deliberately steered clear of Raymond Mays and instead spoke to three people who were friends of his. One of them professed to know Elvira and knew of her preoccupation with numerology. The news was disquieting. Someone who was researching numbers in terms of their power over the lives of racing drivers was not on Mike's preferred guest list at any circuit. It unsettled him even more when, at 10 o'clock that night, he learned that she had taken a close interest into the death of Luigi Musso. His car at Reims had carried the number 22.

Mike's immediate reaction was to leave the hotel and run across the race track into the pits where the mechanics were still at work, unsurprising as it was not out of the ordinary for them to work all night on the eve of a race. He was relieved to discover that his car did not bear the fateful number, but then to his horror he saw that Pete's car did, albeit in a strange way. The actual number of the car was 2, a painted black number inside a white circle. However, since the number appeared twice, both on the right-hand side of the upper front cowling as well as on the left-hand side, the two digits could be read as 22, but only by someone with either an imaginative mind – or a tendency towards paranoia. Since Mike suffered from the latter the impact of what he saw delivered him a sickening blow.

He returned to the hotel, anxious to warn Pete, to get him to protest to the race authority and have the deadly number removed from his car. But he found him with Louise chatting to other drivers. He would be difficult to extract and talked to alone without alerting Louise that something was amiss. In his obsession he connected Carlotta as having somehow persuaded a race official to award Pete the dangerous number.

Mike was not that unhinged that he was without logic. He knew that Pete would hardly believe his story about Elvira Massingham and her connection with Carlotta. He would simply laugh it off.

It also occurred to Mike that instilling Pete with his own fears might have the counter productive effect of disturbing his equilibrium before the race, hardly conducive in itself to him having a safe race.

Mike went outside, took out and breathed into his brown paper bag. Then, with calm descending, tried to reason further with himself, in putting the pros and cons. Pete was regarded as one of the safest drivers, if not the safest, was he not? There had never been a complaint against him, either from a fellow driver or from any race authority. Then, as if to prove that he was not freaking out, Mike tried telling himself not to be so stupid. A number was no more than a number. How could it have any significance? What the fuck was he worrying about? But he still worried – and intensely.

Then a shaft of pain hit him in the guts. All hope of talking to Pete was gone as he was forced back to his room where he took a painkiller. But it failed to work. He came out into the corridor bent on seeing Duncan, hoping that he might know of someone who could assist without alerting any race official.

Grimacing, he set off down the corridor and was met by Taffy on his way to bed. He stopped at the pain etched into Mike's face and expressed his concern. A descendant of a well-known aristocratic German family, he listened to Mike telling him that he had a gallstone problem. Taffy, understanding why Mike was anxious to keep it a secret, politely interrupted him to say that he would immediately telephone his cousin, a doctor who lived 20 miles from the circuit. The upshot was that Taffy drove a 40 mile return journey to return with a powerful brand of pain killing tablets and with the instruction that Mike took one that night but under no circumstances must he take any before the race.

Mike was moved by Taffy's generosity. It was yet another debt with which he was landed. The patient had not liked 'Krauts' until now.

Mike was one of the generation who had lived through the years of the Nazi domination of Europe and believed, as many did, that all Germans were responsible. He had now changed his mind and warmly embraced Taffy.

He thought about Pete again, but he and Louise were now probably in bed. He was faced with the old problem of trying to communicate with him without Louise becoming suspicious. Anything that might upset her on the eve of a race that she dreaded, had to be avoided at all costs.

Mike lay on his bed and tried to relax before sleep.

Around the forest a large crowd was already assembling under the stars, many camping out overnight. The build up would continue through dawn into the late morning. The continuing duel between Mike and Stirling had intensified the interest of racing fans everywhere, as well as the wider European public. The Ring in its densely forested setting, with 172 corners and a 1,000ft drop from its highest to its lowest point, would prove a stern test of machine and driver.

Mike feared it as he had the Monza 500. What had the consultant said to him about g-forces and his internal organs?

Enzo Ferrari put a late night call through to Tavoni. It was not about positions on the grid as they were already established, Mike on pole, Tony Brooks alongside, adjacent to him Stirling and Pete. Basil Cardew had already scrawled on his note pad 'A case of the Vanwall meat in the Ferrari sandwich'. No, Enzo's call was simply to ask Tavoni if Carlotta was well as he had sent her 'two letters about Luigi' and had not received a reply. He said he was concerned that she remained safe within the team. His real reason, of course, was the need to calm his frustration. Why wasn't she responding to his overtures?

Tavoni reassured Enzo that she was, indeed, with the team, was seemingly composed and calm, that her bereavement had not prompted any more suicidal tendencies. Enzo, partially satisfied, had to settle for that.

Carlotta went to bed, curling up in pleasure at the prospect of putting a spell once more on Hawthorn. It was a thought as appealing as iced champagne.

Mike lay in bed, still trying to sleep. Had he known that Carlotta had not been involved in a plot to fix car numbers he might have relaxed that night. He had rid himself of the pain, thanks to Taffy, but could not rid himself of his niggling fears.

He took a sleeping tablet, a barbiturate. After 10 minutes he blacked out.

# **Chapter** Eight

**The Nürburgring, Sunday 3 August 1958**

Mike had slept well. Surprisingly, the after effects of the barbiturate had largely dissipated when, at 9am, he made his way to Pete and Louise's room where he would join with them for breakfast. It was also usual for him to wake up Pete, a notoriously long sleeper.

Louise was wide awake and dressed, sitting in front of the mirror and brushing her hair when he knocked at the door.

'How's the Golden Boy?' she asked with a smile.

'He's great mon ami "matess". How are you?' He gave her a kiss.

'I'm terrific. Going to be a nice day. Sunshine all the way.'

He went to the bed and tapped the sleeping Pete on the shoulder. 'Wakey wakey matey!'

'Bugger off,' Pete murmured.

Mike pulled back the sheet that covered his shoulders. 'Out,' he commanded.

Another moan from Pete. Louise went to stand the other side of the bed from Mike. 'One-two-three!' she ordered. Together they ripped back the bedclothes.

'You rotters.' Pete opened his eyes, crawled slowly out of bed and then wandered to collect his dressing gown from the back of a chair. Putting it on, he plonked his pillow upright against the head board and then got back into bed to sit with his back resting against it.

'Breakfast and sharpish,' he commanded.

'Bollocks,' said Mike.

It was all ritual.

After a full breakfast Pete hastened to start work on a wooden puzzle, the aim being to fit all the parts together to make a complete circle. He was constantly buying such teasers and it was his habit each race morning to spend as much time as it took in order to find the solution. For a break he would dip into a truck magazine, it being his ambition, one day, to race them in competition. He would not take lunch as was also his custom. For Pete, mental alertness was all important. He had set himself a deadline of 1pm for completing the puzzle.

Mike watched him fiddling with the wooden pieces, feeling less anxious than the previous night, the fear of numbers seeming faintly ridiculous in the bright and airy room into which the sunlight streamed. There was also the sound of a guitar being played from somewhere nearby and that, for him, always helped create an optimistic mood.

He watched Louise, taking in her neatness of figure and apparently calm repose, as she sat at the table going methodically through her diary, ticking off items and altering others. He was relieved that he had not upset her, to have thrown her by exhibiting his own fears would have been unforgivable. Yet he found he still had that fear, but with no possible prospect now of changing the number, it being far too late in the pre-race countdown, he went downstairs to join the number of drivers who were spending the morning in the hotel lounge, either chatting or reading.

Mike was there relaxing in an armchair when, just after 12.30pm, there came a shout from the staircase and soon afterwards Pete burst into the room holding the result of his labours, a completed wooden circle. Cackling, he held it up for all to see. There was a chorus of cheering from the assembled drivers.

'Bloody genius,' said Stirling, glancing up from an old copy of *Reader's Digest*.

'Give the man a medal,' said Harry.

'Too right,' said Pete. 'Do you lot realise just how bloody difficult this is?'

'A kid could do it,' said Stuart, grinning.

'What!' Pete looked offended. 'I will give you my next one. I will bet you five pounds that you don't do it in two hours. Done?'

'No,' Stuart said. 'I hate puzzles.'

Louise entered the room with a tray holding two cups of coffee. One was for Fangio's girlfriend Beba, the other for herself. She saw Pete in a highly chuffed state, placed the tray down on a table and went back to fetch one more. On her return she put out her hand to Pete, asking for the puzzle while offering him a cup of coffee in exchange.

'Break it up, let me have a go,' she said.

Pete, theatrically, pulled himself away, impersonating Laurence Olivier. 'What? Are you insane woman? Out, out! This is mine. I did this! Are you aware that this is the most difficult puzzle in the whole history of civilisation? And I, only I, have done it.'

Amid the general laughter, Mike grinned, stood up and hugged him.

'You're the winner,' he said, then grabbed the puzzle and tossed it to Louise.

'Eh! Don't you dare!' Pete levelled a threatening finger at Louise.

She pretended to snap it open.

'Don't – !'

It helped pass the time.

*  *  *  *  *

Mike and Pete sat in the motor home patiently going through the chore of sticking see-through strips across their vizors. Louise, as usual, busied herself around the kitchenette. Suddenly the calm was shattered by the rasp of a formula one engine bursting into life, only to immediately falter and die.

Seconds later the same engine broke out again with another rasp, this time developing into a roar. As if stimulated by the noise another engine took life. During the next 15 minutes other engines joined the chorus. The German Grand Prix was on count down.

At 2pm Stuart Lewis-Evans was at the door of the motor home with yet another body belt for Mike.

'Stuart, thanks,' said Mike. 'I forgot. What would I do without you?'

Stuart grinned. 'Lose?'

They all laughed.

Mike suddenly stopped laughing as Stuart left, his face tightening into a painful grimace. He went quickly outside to avoid being seen by Pete and Louise, but stepped straight into the path of Taffy who was approaching the motor home from the pits. It was impossible for Mike to hide his distress. Even if he were charged with the excitement of the race he knew that the adrenalin blocking out this pain would not be enough.

'Mike,' Taffy said in sympathy. 'Is it bad?'

'Yeah,' Mike said. 'I've got to take one. Is it okay? I can't...'

He broke off in agony. 'Taffy, can you get me some water please? I don't want Louise to see.'

Taffy did as he bid, returning with a glass of water that he pretended he had taken outside for himself. Mike popped a pill into his mouth, followed by a swig of water. 'Thanks.'

'Mike,' said Taffy, worried. 'I don't think you should race. Tell them…'

'No.' Mike cutting in, made a gesture. 'I'll be okay. I'll be fine. Don't worry.'

* * * * *

Carlotta, wearing the same clothes as at Silverstone, sat on the pit counter watching Mike on the front row of the grid. Then she hid a smile as she saw him glance towards her. But this time he did not jerk his head away, but stared resolutely back. And that was it as far as he was concerned. The challenge had been met. He would not look a second time.

After the warm up, with engines revving all around him, Mike focused on the braking zone ahead. The pain had died down, and he felt calm, the drug doing its work. At least he could think clearly and without stress. Despite being on pole position he knew that he had to come out of the blocks as fast as Stirling, who sat next to his immediate neighbour, Tony Brooks. Pete was on the outside of Stirling.

As the flag was raised 20 formula one engines broke into a snarling, threatening rage.

'Hold…hold…' Mike went through his father's litany, his brain devoted to dealing with his feet, the left carefully balancing the clutch, the other the throttle. Any nervous twitch and he could lose it in a stall.

Carlotta stared intently at Mike, then bared the tips of her teeth in frustration as he refused to look.

The flag dropped.

He was away, but not with his usual precision, dropping into third place behind Stirling and Tony Brooks, the latter first into the South Curve, closely followed by Stirling with Harry Schell, Mike and Pete trailing. At the end of the lap, Stirling, by virtue of having hit each braking zone exactly on the sweet spot, had taken the lead being six seconds ahead of Mike, an astonishing lead in such a short space of time. On lap two he broke Mike's record set the previous day. At the end of lap three he had extended his lead even more, being now 17 seconds ahead of Pete who had since overtaken Mike.

The race continued with Mike trying to hang on to Pete's tail, but the drug continued to hold him back. He simply was not 'on the pace'.

As lap four began Mike faced up to the fact that his future still lay in the hands of Stirling, whose performance today dismissed any doubts that he still entertained the notion of surrender that he had voiced after his breakdown at Silverstone.

And then fortune stepped in to boost Mike's hopes as the Vanwall jinx struck once again. The magneto attached to Stirling's engine failed. Its job of generating and delivering a high voltage charge to the sparking plugs, was over as the car simply ran to a standstill.

Disaster for one, joy for another. Mike's spirits rose as he passed Stirling stepping out of his stricken car.

Pete Collins also got the message and with Stirling retired concentrated his thoughts on helping Mike to victory, but this time he would be careful. There would be no repeat of Silverstone when he had been so far ahead of Mike that it had been impossible to relinquish his lead without incurring the wrath of the public and made the subject of a steward's enquiry.

But there was still another Vanwall in the race and posing a threat to Mike's chances of outright victory. Tony Brooks lay 30 seconds behind Pete, but suspected that Mike and Pete were working in tandem with each other and that Pete's generosity of spirit was not beyond helping his teammate to victory. Tony harboured the hope that if Pete allowed Mike to overtake there might just arise the possibility of them losing time in the manoeuvre. And so he began a charge intending to get as close to Mike as possible.

His gamble proved its worth. On lap six Pete had already slowed down a little to keep Mike in his slipstream. And Mike, with the drug affecting his reaction times, was content to stay there, trying to relax his body by merely keeping station. The manoeuvre involved in overtaking always sent up his blood pressure and with an hour and a half left of racing time he had to take every measure he could to conserve his energies. He reminded himself that only one point separated the first from the second place at the end of the race. With Stirling no longer in contention any points that he won would be a bonus. One point dropped would be a premium worth paying in order to ensure that he finished behind Pete.

But mon ami Pete, not knowing that Mike was affected by the side effects of a strong pain killer, was already working out the best place to allow Mike to overtake. On lap seven, on one of the lonely stretches, he put up an arm and beckoned Mike with a 'come on, pass me' gesture.

But Mike failed to respond. This worried Pete, was it that Mike was in trouble? There was a hiatus between Pete slowing down and Mike's failure to respond. And so Pete slowed down even more. This caused Mike to have no option but to draw alongside and indulge in gestures indicating that he wanted to follow, not lead. In all this Pete became confused and even more time was lost.

As this little drama was being acted out on the back straight Tony Brooks was making up lost ground. As he hit the start of the next lap the lap board held out to him by his mechanic bore the symbol for 'Hurry Up', meaning that he was catching the two Ferraris. He responded accordingly. Although his car was slower than the Dinos on the three kilometre straight it had better suspension and disc brakes giving it an advantage in braking and cornering. In utilising all his skills, allied to a mechanical advantage, by the end of the seventh lap Tony lay close behind Mike who was still tailing a frustrated Pete.

Pete saw the Vanwall in his mirrors and decided that Mike's best chance now lay in him intervening between his car and Tony's. He wanted to hold back the Vanwall, not by cheating but by gearing himself up to the challenge of cornering. He would take up the racing line but in so doing ensure that he was as fast as Tony into and out of the turns. It would take all his skill and effort.

At the next corner his intention was to brake slightly on exit, trusting that Mike's momentum would be so great that he would have no choice but to overtake. On the approach he glanced in his mirror to ensure that he was close enough to initiate the manoeuvre. It was vital that, in handing Mike the lead, there would be no slip up as Tony would be sure to pounce if given half a chance.

But, yet again, Pete's quick 'come on' gesture and a quick dab at the brakes failed to draw Mike past him. His spirits dropped as the inevitable occurred on the ninth lap. As they went into the North Turn, with Pete repeating his brake and 'pass me' gesture, the Vanwall dived inside Mike's Ferrari to grab second place.

With only three car lengths between them, the Ferrari-Vanwall-Ferrari express sped through the Ring's switchback curves until they reached the next straight.

Maybe it was the adrenalin flowing through Mike's veins – or was it sheer bloody mindedness? – that gave him the edge to power past Tony. It was a short lived success. Within two minutes Tony, using his better suspension and disc brakes, once again overtook Mike, this time on the North Turn.

Pete led by a whisker on the 10th lap when Mike made another passing move into second place. But either his adrenalin burst had dissipated, or his brain's neurotransmitters were still on a go-slow, but he was unable to prevent Tony from overtaking him once more, this time on the South Turn. There, the roar of the crowd, could be heard over the car engines.

Then Tony caught up with Pete and went ahead into the lead. The public address system bellowed out the race commentary via loudspeakers attached to trees around the forest cloaked circuit. Spectators were agog with excitement, especially the British contingent who were seeing the German Grand Prix dominated by three English drivers. The patriotic Italians in the crowd – and there were many thousands – were equally excited by their beloved blood red Ferraris dicing with a car painted British racing green.

Tony continued with his attempt to take advantage of his car's superior braking and cornering but Pete and Mike were still up to the task of preventing him from establishing a dominant lead. He was still trying to shake off the two Ferraris hot on his tail when they began the 11th lap, the threesome hurtling along the twisting race track. The excitement mounted around the circuit as each section of the crowd strung out over 14 miles of track cheered on either the battling Vanwall or the two Ferraris. The whole of the grandstand was on its feet, shouting and applauding the combatants as they roared past.

As they left Brunnchen, the three cars were still in close formation. On approaching the corner by the Pflanzgarten each driver's routine action was to drop into a fast third gear and then into second. In the dip that lay before the uphill rise to the corner they would take their feet off the brakes momentarily, then dab at them again. They would enter the right hander while still accelerating.

Tony was on the apex of the bend when Pete approached the corner. Mike concentrated on his racing line and as he did so he saw Pete's car drift wide, then slide with its rear left wheel along a grassy low bank. There was a glimpse of dust. Further into the corner the dust cloud as seen in his mirror continued to swell. Where was Pete? Mike was round the corner before he realised that he had crashed.

Mike slammed on his brakes, almost stopping as he tried to look round, but there was nothing to see apart from the billowing dust. What he had failed to see was the Ferrari whipping over, then standing on its nose before striking the fencing.

Mike had to find a marshal. He could see none in the immediate vicinity and so he drove on in fearful anxiety. Then he spotted a marshal standing within a refuge and on approach rapidly crashed down from top to bottom gear. As the rev counter needle whipped into the red zone there was a mighty bang and the engine exploded. As the car came to a halt he stepped out and ran back to the marshal pointing from where he had come.

'Accident!' He screamed.

The non-English speaking marshal stared.

Mike went to the wooden telephone box, opened it, grabbed the phone urging the marshal to take it.

'Tell them! Collins! Collins! Ferrari crash! Find him! Where is Collins?'

The marshal frowned and took the phone. As he spoke Mike eyed the metal fencing that separated the refuge from the forest with a view to crossing it, but saw that the top edges were laced with barbed wire. In any case the closely packed fir trees that lay immediately behind the fencing were virtually impenetrable. But somehow he had to get back to Pete and started to edge himself along the grassy ledge that bordered the track while clinging to the fence. The marshal grabbed him and pulled him back into the refuge.

'Okay!' Mike screamed. 'But find out about Collins! Is he injured!'

The marshal spoke into the telephone.

Mike sank to the ground, in anguish, clutching his face.

# **Chapter** Nine

Before Pete brought Louise to her first motor race her immediate reaction was to voice her fears: 'Pete, how can I wait to see if you come round on each lap? I'm going to be terrified.'

In answer Pete introduced her to Beba and Lulu, the two women who had prevented Carlotta from committing suicide. They told Louise that they understood how she felt. Like her they had both experienced that same kind of fear, assuring her that there was a remedy. The secret lay in being tasked with the job of recording the lap times of two drivers. Should Pete 'go missing' during a race she must concentrate on recording the lap times of the other driver, keeping her busy until the waiting was over. Nearly all the wives or girlfriends performed that service for their man. It served to help him and it helped them.

No, it was not an academic exercise, they said. Her work could have a real input in terms of assessing car, driver and team performance. Knowing this, she would be too worried about making a mistake to allow herself to get in a state about his whereabouts. In any case it was commonplace for the missing to find themselves unable to move from the place where their car had broken down until after the race. If a driver did manage to return to the pits, say after half an hour's absence, it was usually by navigating his way back round a packed and obstacle littered circuit. Beba and Lulu assured Louise that if Pete continued not to show up it was not cause for alarm.

'It happens all the time,' laughed Lulu. 'Don't worry. Beba and me have been doing it for years!'

And so, on this sunny day, 10 minutes after Pete had 'gone missing' Louise maintained her calmness by switching her attention solely to Taffy, her 'other driver'.

She was performing this routine task when, suddenly, a shadow fell across the lapboard that sat on her knee. Catching her breath, she looked up. From over Tavoni's shoulder the sun shone into her eyes causing her to put up a hand. Unable to see his expression his first word drove a dagger through her heart.

'Pete...'

'No.' The word came out in a faint voice.

'Don't worry,' Tavoni quickly reassured her. 'He's okay. His car has broken down. Don't worry he's walking back.'

He had told her as much as he knew. It was not rare for a missing driver to be reported as uninjured following an accident when in reality he had serious injuries – and vice versa. Tavoni had been told initially that Pete was only 'badly bruised' following his accident but the message had not come from the medical centre, but via links starting with an uncomprehending marshal, so that when Tavoni received the news it was a complete distortion of the facts.

However, Louise had not been subject to misinformation before and so accepted the news without question. She took a long and very deep breath, stretched out an arm to waggle her finger tips as a gesture of thanks and exhaled slowly in relief. She was further reassured when Tavoni returned 10 minutes later to say that Mike's car had also broken down and that the two of them were stuck somewhere in the forest for the duration of the race. 'Somebody will have a glass of beer for them,' he joked.

She forced a smile.

The reality could not have been more different. Mike's desperate and demanding order that the marshal relay his message about Pete to Race Control, had not produced anything positive. Unable to understand Mike's desperate plea the marshal had merely transmitted a message that Hawthorn was out of the race with a broken down car.

He added that Collin's car had also broken down and was lying on the track in a dangerous place. Even if Race Control had been asked about Pete's physical condition it was always the case that urgent communications regarding track safety took precedence over queries relating to a missing driver. An accident at a blind turn could pose a great danger in terms of a damaged car and its debris lying around. The driver's whereabouts and state of health came second to the urgent decision that had to be made to avoid a much greater calamity. Should the injured driver's position not be immediately located then the search for him would take place when the emergency was out of the way. In Pete's case there was no race emergency, but the Medical Centre had not been informed of any injury relating to him and so its rescue helicopter remained on its pad.

Mike continued to suffer. Forced to wait three quarters of an hour without knowing if Pete were alive or dead he spent most of the time pleading with, exhorting, but finally succumbing to the marshal, whose irritation with Mike was now visible.

Meanwhile, completely unaware that Pete had been involved in an accident, Louise completed her lap chart. She recorded Taffy as having finished in fourth place behind Maurice Trintignant, whose wife Lulu, after kissing him in celebration, went over to ask her of news about Pete.

Louise, entirely unfazed, said he was out 'boozing' with Mike somewhere. They both laughed. Louise remembered to congratulate Lulu on Maurice's achievement in finishing third.

As Lulu was returning to her pits she noticed Duncan Hamilton standing motionless and staring at Louise. She had seen that kind of look before, one showing caution and hesitancy, both driven by fear. She turned round quickly to see Louise notice Duncan and with a smile step towards him.

And then the smile died, his expression rooting her to the spot. The lap chart dropped from her fingers. She fumbled backwards to touch the chair she had just vacated and dropped into it, the colour draining from her face.

Lulu rushed to grab hold of her, glaring at Duncan defensively.

He came slowly forwards, finally crouching down to Louise's eye level and then placed a tentative hand on her arm.

'Pete's had an accident Louise. They're taking him to hospital.' Duncan's eyes flickered. He dropped his gaze momentarily.

'How...?' The question caught in Louise's throat. 'How bad?'

'I think he's got a head injury. They're taking him to Bonn. There's a specialist clinic there. It – er – deals with head injuries.' Then he added. 'It's the best.'

Lulu gripped Louise tighter still.

'I want to go with him!' Louise tried to stand up, but Duncan stayed her with his hand. 'You can't Louise. I asked. It's only a small helicopter. They're putting him on board now.'

'Duncan?' It was a keening sound that she uttered, pleading with him to tell her it was not true, that it was a mistake, that it could not have happened, that it was a nightmare that would suddenly end. Then she tore herself away from Lulu and ran into the paddock.

* * * * *

Mike had put up with enough shit for the day. Even as the last car on the track powered towards him on its final lap he set off, scowling and raising a fist as the marshal repeatedly shouted at him to return. He was slowed down momentarily by the blast of the car's wake as it shot past him, but then he recovered enough energy to race to the corner, arriving in a state of near exhaustion. He looked for Pete's car but it had just been removed by a breakdown truck.

There was a crowd gathered. Mike picked out a marshal's arm band and gesticulated at him. 'Pete Collins? Collins? Where's Collins?'

A number of people, spectators mostly, jabbered their answers, some Italian, some German. But the marshal spoke some English. In the confusion Mike could make out the words 'ambulance' and 'Medical Centre'. Quietening the rest, Mike urgently asked him to explain what had happened. The marshal said that he had just arrived on the scene to be told that Collins had been thrown from the car and had been taken to the Medical Centre.

Mike was in shock and instead of hitching a lift back to the pits where he would learn of Pete's condition, scrambled over the broken down fencing to make the illogical move of searching for evidence that would point to Pete being safe and well, apart from a few cuts and bruises. He first spotted a brown crash helmet lying at the edge of the tree line, partially hidden by churned up fir needles. And only a short distance away lay a glove. He picked up each item and examined them carefully. Neither were stained with blood, not even traces of it. Alright, the helmet was dented and cracked a little, but that was its job, wasn't it, to protect the head? In his dreamlike state he was unable to process anything beyond that simple thought.

He stuffed the glove into his pocket and was about to climb back over the fencing when he stopped. A few yards to his left was a black shoe. He went to it, paused and then picked it up. This, too, showed no sign that Pete had been injured. He hesitated, then dropped it by instinct without even reasoning why. Within seconds of getting back to the trackside he had already obliterated it from his mind. It no longer existed.

A marshal's road car came to stop at the corner and gave him a lift back to the pits.

On arrival he dashed across to the Medical Centre, a building on the edge of the line of pits. Outside stood a helicopter, about to take off. A cluster of spectators, including Louise comforted by Duncan and Tavoni, stood watching. The helicopter rotors began to turn, the draft causing heads and shoulders to be averted from the stinging dust. But Louise did not move, merely closing her eyes and then opening them again when the blast had died down. She watched the helicopter as it banked into the sun, heading west. It was then that Mike went to her.

'Louise.'

She turned at the sound of his voice and looked at him, her face blank. Then she stared at the helmet in his hands.

Mike framed words of explanation on his lips, but was slow of thinking and Tavoni cut in.

'They're taking him to the Bonn University Clinic. Louise wanted to go with him but there was no room. I'm taking her.'

Holding her close with one arm Tavoni escorted her to his car, a mirror image of Reims when he had driven Carlotta to the hospital. Mike watched them go, surrounded by the press and photographers.

'Come on mate.'

A hand touched his elbow. It was Duncan who had been joined by Harry Schell and Stuart.

'I'm driving,' said Harry. 'Let's go and change.'

Mike wondered what he meant.

'Can't go to a hospital like that.'

Mike glanced down at his dirty white trousers and oil stained gabardine jacket. He shook his head. 'I'm okay.'

'No you're not.' Duncan was firm. 'First you've got to drink water. The roads are going to be choked anyway. No need to rush.'

His prophecy materialised. Tavoni's car, with Louise as passenger, crawled out of the circuit to join a traffic jam pointing north-west. She stared at the faces in the slow moving cars around her, people who had watched Pete race, possibly knew that he was injured. How could they chat and smile?

Mike's journey, that started 30 minutes later, was no less agonising. It took three hours for them to reach the outskirts of Bonn and during that time neither Duncan, Harry nor Stuart said anything apart from uttering brief directions as they approached the city. Mike sat in silence the whole way, the helmet on his lap. When he had entered the Sporthotel it was the helmet that had bewildered the onlookers. It had been beyond anyone to divine the reason, that he carried it because subconsciously he knew it to be Pete's property and meant therefore, that he was alive.

The Bonn University Clinic was famous for its work in neurology. Dr Peter Roettgen was one of Germany's leading brain surgeons. By the time Tavoni and Louise arrived at the Clinic he had done his work, which was minimal. The receptionist called for the doctor who came out to meet Louise and Tavoni. Gently he suggested that they sat down in a side room.

Louise, before sitting down, expressed her confusion. She could not understand. Where was Pete? Why were they stopping her seeing him?

Dr Roettgen waited for her to sit down before answering the question. He spoke quietly and sympathetically. 'I am sorry but your husband has gone. He would have died without pain. It was very sudden when the accident happened.'

Louise stared at him, frowning. How could Pete be dead? Why had they brought him all this way to a hospital in Bonn if he was dead? Why had she travelled all that way if not to see him? It did not make sense. She stood up.

'I must see him,' she declared. 'It's a mistake.'

'You are sure that you would like to see him?'

'Yes. I'll prove it. I must.'

She was taken back into the corridor, to a room at the far end where Dr Roettgen stopped to have a quiet word with Tavoni, who nodded and stepped backwards in order to let Louise enter before him.

The room contained only a table. On it lay a body covered by a white sheet. Tavoni stood closely behind Louise. He placed his hands on her upper arms and maintained a firm hold as Dr Roettgen slowly peeled back the sheet.

Louise gave a sharp intake of breath. The left arm of the body had lolled over the side of the table and dropped below the edge of the sheet to reveal the hand. On it was Pete's wedding ring. As her legs gave way, Tavoni was ready and gave her enough support to extract her from the room and back to reception.

Mike, Harry and Duncan arrived in Bonn 40 minutes later. There was some confusion about the whereabouts of the clinic, but eventually they crossed the Rhine bridge at Ramersdorf and headed for Sigmund-Freud Strasse in the centre of which was the Neurological Clinic, a department of the larger University Hospital.

On arrival they were directed to reception. But no sign of Louise. They were told that she had left with 'Herr Tavoni'. The receptionist called for Dr Roettgen.

Mike's state of denial was as strong as Louise's had been, protesting that Pete could not possibly be dead. Just as Louise had declared, he said, 'It must be a mistake'.

Once again, Dr Roettgen went through the procedure of taking the bereaved into the viewing room. Mike watched as the sheet was drawn back. But, unlike Louise, he felt no sudden weakness of the legs because what he saw made him angry.

It was bloody stupid, some sort of sick joke. Where were Pete's injuries? There was no mark that he could see on Pete's body, other than some bruising on the right arm. How could he possibly be dead?

Dr Roettgen calmly pointed to the right-hand side of the corpse's neck that was in shadow, implying that Mike should take a closer look, which he did by bending down. He saw that the skin around the base of the neck was the colour of deep and dark vermilion. As he drew up straight Dr Roettgen informed him that Pete had died from his spinal cord being completely severed, that his death had been instantaneous.

Mike stared at him for some time and then, dreamlike, retreated slowly back into the corridor.

Duncan, Stuart and Harry, seeing that his jaw had dropped and his face whiten, made a move towards him thinking he was about to faint, but Mike rested his back against the wall and after a few seconds began gradually to slip down until he sat slumped on the floor, his legs stretched out. His fingers loosened their grip on the helmet and it rolled on to the corridor floor, made a rocking sound and then lay still.

Duncan, Harry and Stuart stood around looking uncertain. The receptionist understood the situation and called for a nurse to administer a sedative. But Mike refused to take it.

It was 7pm.

\* \* \* \* \*

At 9.25pm they arrived back at the Sporthotel where they escorted Mike back to his room. He enquired about Louise and was told that she was being looked after by Beba and Lulu.

Stuart nipped out to go down to the bar. When he returned with a bottle of brandy Duncan had already started to pack Mike's things.

A knock came at the door. It was Tony Brooks, the most reluctant of all race winners.

His condolences were deeply felt. He said he would have given up not only his victory but also the sport to have seen Pete alive and well.

Mike could say little in return apart from 'Thanks mate'.

There were murmured congratulations for his win from Harry and Stuart.

Tony left. Like many of the drivers who came to offer their sympathies that night, it would be some time before he would renew his enthusiasm for motor racing.

The next to pay their respects was Bernie Ecclestone, the owner of the struggling Connaught team. After expressing his sorrow he declared that enough was enough and that he was going to quit the so-called 'sport'. In his case it would be exactly 12 years before he would return to motor racing.

The shock of bereavement takes various pathways, according to the individual. The feeling of being disconnected from emotion and an inability to think logically is commonplace. Mike had not yet left the stage of disbelief. Grief would come at some point. But there was something else that threatened him that night and which had nothing to do with the stages of bereavement. It was something that had plagued him ever since the Le Mans tragedy, had intensified with the death of Luigi and was now about to get much worse.

It was the arrival of Taffy that started the process. It was a remark he made that, although not immediately registering, settled uncomfortably in the lower strata of Mike's consciousness. Taffy said that he had spoken to the race scrutineers and that they had found 'nothing wrong with Pete's car'. He went on to say that his own car had suffered from brake failure on the second lap, believing it to have been caused by a malfunction of the brake fluid reservoir. There was an automatic adjustment that it was designed to make and which, he claimed, had become faulty.

'Could this have caused Pete's crash?'

He said the scrutineers had already considered it but had dismissed it as a possible cause.

'But what else could have caused it?' said Stuart after Taffy had left. 'That corner's routine.'

Stirling Moss came to offer his condolences. He said he could not understand what he had been told because 'Pete was such a safe driver...'

'Pete was such a safe driver.' It was Stirling's statement that triggered Mike's dormant brain into life. Until then he had not been able to make proper connections, to draw conclusions or inferences from separate situations, to draw them together and form a conclusion. Up till now his thought processes had been as dead as his feelings. But they had now awoken, thanks to Stirling.

Back in a state of awareness, capable of thinking beyond the immediate here and now, Mike linked what Taffy had said to Stirling's comment. Pete was 'a safe driver' and there was 'nothing wrong with the car'. The phrases continued to echo in his head: 'Jesus,' he breathed. 'Oh my God.' He put his head in his hands.

'Mike. What's wrong?' Stuart said sharply, bending down, staring into his face.

'Mike? What's happened?'

Duncan exchanged glances with Stuart and Harry. He too, bent down to Mike.

'What is it?' he said.

To everyone's surprise Mike sprang upright and went quickly out of the room without a word of explanation. Stuart exchanged sharp looks with

Harry and Duncan before going quickly after him, entering the corridor in time to see Mike turning off to hurry down the staircase into the lobby. Stuart quickly followed him down to find him talking to the woman clerk at the reception desk. The conversation was loud enough for Stuart to overhear her give Mike the room number of the former Grand Prix driver, Karl Kling.

Stuart went up to Mike as he turned away from the desk.

'Mike…'

But he was cut off by Mike grimacing at him and putting up a hand to mean that he had no time to talk.

Stuart watched him hurry through the double doors that led to the ground floor bedrooms. He went back to report to Duncan and Harry. Something clearly had scared Mike, he told them, something to do with Karl Kling…

Karl Kling, they all knew, was a racing car scrutineer who would have taken part in the investigation into Pete's car to try and discover what, if any, malfunction or mechanical failure had caused the accident.

'Dead weird,' said Harry. 'You any idea Stuart?'

Stuart shook his head. He knew far more than Harry about Mike's problems but could think of nothing connected with Pete's crash.

And neither could Duncan. It was no use chasing Mike, he said. They'd simply have to wait for the outcome of whatever new crisis had arisen.

But Stuart could not leave it alone. 'Look. It was like turning on a light. Mike had been shocked. He was dead slow wasn't he, like he had been hit on the head? But as soon as Stirling said Pete was a safe driver I saw his face. Did you see that?' asked Stuart of them both. 'He got all agitated?'

They all agreed it was a puzzle.

'Yeah, a really weird one,' said Harry. He said that he was surprised that Mike had talked to a scrutineer without first clearing it through Tavoni.

Mike was fortunate to find Karl in his room and was made immediately welcome. He had been a fellow competitor against Mike four or five years back and they had become friendly, but not before Mike checked out what he had done in the war.

It so happened that Karl had served in the Luftwaffe as a service engineer of German fighter aircraft. This was not so bad as, post war, a few German fighter pilots were known to have made contact with their old enemies of the Royal Air Force.

Mike was relying on his friendship with Karl to produce an answer. He asked him urgently about Taffy's brakes. Could it have been that Pete's own braking system had become faulty? 'Pete was right in front of me,' he added. 'I went into the corner on the right line. He didn't. It must have been his brakes, Karl. Or steering.'

Karl, a fluent English speaker, was surprised at the urgency behind Mike's questioning and asked him the reason.

Mike immediately apologised and said that Pete was his best mate and he did not like to think it had been driver error that had killed him. He was telling the truth but there was far more to it than that, but was unable to tell Karl what it was. Instead he put to him Taffy's concern that the crash might have been caused by a faulty brake fuel reservoir.

Karl repeated the official finding, that they had taken into account the problem with the brake fluid reservoir and found nothing wrong with it.

'Mike, you must accept that we looked at everything. We examined the reservoir. Every moving part, you know we do. Nothing wrong with the brakes, tyres, steering, nothing at all.' He went on to say that a senior engineer from Daimler Benz had been present at the scrutiny and had concurred with the official findings. There was no doubt whatsoever that Pete had died by making a mistake on cornering.

Mike was left staring at him. It was the confirmation that he dreaded. But because there was so much at stake he found himself putting the question again.

'Karl, it had to be the brakes or steering. I was behind him. Pete didn't make the turn. I couldn't see what happened because I was cornering myself, but I know how wide he ran. It was stupid. A novice wouldn't have made that mistake. He'd never have gone into a corner like that.'

Karl remained cool under pressure. 'Mike, I understand. But we found nothing wrong with the brakes. On the Dino the reservoir only switches on when the brake linings are worn down. Peter's brake linings were not.' He gave a shrug of the shoulders and an apologetic smile.

But Mike still had to persist. 'Okay, but why did Taffy have his brakes fail on his second lap when the brake linings would not be worn down? How do you account for that Karl?'

'I'm sorry Mike, but his car is a separate matter from Peter's. He didn't crash so it's not a matter for us but for the team. You know that.' Karl's tone had become a little more official. 'I can only tell you about his car. Yes, we discussed the possibility that Peter's brakes were at fault. But every check that we made showed that they were in good working order. In any case the brake linings were not worn down enough to cause any problem with the automatic adjustment on the brake fluid reservoir. You have to accept that the only conclusion we could draw was that it was due to driver error.'

Mike was silenced, but continued to stare at Karl until finally, his challenges ran out. In apology he patted Karl on the shoulder, thanked him and left.

Exhausted and deeply troubled, he decided to take the lift back to his room on the second floor. He pressed the call button and stood back to watch the bronze finger on the fan shaped dial above the doors. It was unmoving, stuck at three.

The sound of doors opening and closing far above echoed down the lift shaft. He pressed the button again and the finger began to move, but upwards not down.

Forced to wait, he leant against the wall and experienced a resurgence of the self pity he had felt at Reims after Luigi's death, but worse. The malevolent fates had decided that he had not suffered enough, that now another death lay at his door, that of his closest and best friend, his mate. There would be no going back to his room to sit down at the dressing table to construct an escape this time. No aide memoire would come to his rescue. He had needed Karl Kling to tell him that Pete's car had been at fault. That had not happened and the conclusion had rightly pointed to driver error. What Karl did not know was that Pete had been watching out for him in his mirrors throughout the race as he had done at Silverstone and had threatened to do at the Ring. On approaching the corner at the Pflanzgarten he had made the fatal mistake of looking once too often. It would have only taken one glance, one second in which to travel so far beyond his braking zone that it had required the steering wheel to be wrenched over to make the turn-in, causing the tail of the car to break away. The cloud of dust had hidden from view its collision with the low banking, its flip upwards and Pete hurled out of the car into the trees.

Pete had died helping him.

The finger on the dial paused at number three. There was the sound of doors opening. He needed Duncan, not Stuart, not now. It had to be Duncan, good old Duncan, 'the hail fellow well met' character who liked the rowdiness of the rugby pitch as much as the beer and the risqué songs that followed. He was the guy who saw life as the great adventure, with no time for introspection. Mike needed him, the closest and the strongest…

Doors closed above his head. The lift hummed on its downwards journey and stopped at number two, the number of his floor. He stared at it. Its significance was stunning.

In his anguish he had completely forgotten the number 2. Pete's car was number 2, seen twice as 22.

# **Chapter** Ten

The bar of the Sporthotel was still crowded at 10pm, the air thick with blue smoke.

Lacking was the conviviality of the occasion as was normal following a German Grand Prix. On this night there was plenty of beer being drunk, but Mike and Duncan were nowhere to be seen.

Much of the general discussion had revolved around the accident. Everyone had known by late afternoon that Pete's car, at the time of the crash, had been recorded as race worthy by the scrutineers. The sports writers had been busy. The two senior reporters, Basil Cardew of the *Daily Express* and Peter Lewis of the *Observer*, having sent off their copy, were now engaged in separate conversations, Lewis with Tavoni and Cardew with Von Trips.

Tavoni had hoped that, in passing the scrutineers' verdict to Enzo, it would be enough to satisfy him. However, it was not the case. The Commendatore had declared it to be the blackest day in the history of the Scuderia. Not only was he stricken by the death of his 'adopted son' but he also had to face the redoubled wrath of the church and press for killing two drivers within a month.

After Tavoni's call Enzo had sat down in contemplation. This time, he told himself, he could not rely on his front man to protect him from the public outrage that would be sure to burst forth on the Monday morning. He sent a cable to Tavoni ordering him to seek out everything he could as to the circumstances surrounding the accident, even down to the tiniest detail. He demanded to know everything, what was done and what was not done, what was said and was not said. To be fully prepared was to be fully forearmed.

Tavoni was fortunate in that Lewis, after despatching his copy to the sports desk of the *Observer*, had gone to him with all the evidence that he needed with which to satisfy Enzo's pernickety demands. By sheer good fortune Lewis had been positioned at the apex of the corner near the Pflanzgarten and had seen Pete's Dino racing towards him. On the strength of what happened next – and given that the scrutineers had found no mechanical fault – he had given Tavoni reassurance that no one involved with the Scuderia could, in any way, shape or form, be blamed for the accident. Lewis had actually handed Tavoni a copy of his race report so that he could read it aloud to Enzo that same evening. The beleaguered Commendatore had listened in silence and afterwards expressed his satisfaction with Tavoni's diligence.

As Tavoni talked with Peter Lewis he became aware that the level of conversation had faded in the room and that all eyes were focused on Mike who had just entered, looking pale, a light sheen of perspiration on his forehead. He caught sight of Tavoni, made a move towards him, but hesitated, not wanting what he had to say to his team manager to be shared with Lewis.

Tavoni took in the look of anxiety on Mike's face and his air of exhaustion. Lewis turned round to follow his gaze and on seeing Mike sprang to his feet.

'Mike. I'm so sorry about Pete.'

'Thanks. I'm told you saw it.'

'Yes, I did. I was on the apex. He came straight on. I don't think he even turned in. Mike, I just can't understand it. They say his brakes and steering were okay, A novice wouldn't have made that mistake. You were behind, have you any idea what happened?'

'No.' Mike's reply was brief and Lewis could see that he was more anxious to talk to Tavoni, than a reporter, but he persisted. 'What did you actually see Mike?'

Mike shrugged. 'I didn't see much. I know he was late on the brakes.'

Lewis nodded, 'I think he looked in his mirror, though why I don't know. You don't when you're hitting a corner, do you?'

'When?' Mike sharply picked up on it.

'Just before he turned in – that's if he turned in.'

'Jesus.' Mike spoke faintly.

Lewis stared at him.

Mike shook his head. 'Sorry, Peter but I've got to talk to Tav.'

'Oh, okay. Sorry Mike. ' Lewis dug a card out of his pocket. 'When you get home I'm doing Pete's obit for the paper. Do you mind if I give you a ring?'

Mike nodded and took the card. 'Okay.'

Lewis briefly touched his arm and then left, threading his way out of the bar in which the normal level of conversation had, by now, been resumed.

Mike sat down in the chair that Lewis had vacated. He paused a moment, and then spoke directly. 'Tav, I've got to know something.'

The normally studious and ascetic looking Tavoni, who normally drank little, sipped the last drops of his treble whisky. 'Mike, it was Peter Lewis who told me all I needed to know. My report to Enzo was based on it.'

'I know that,' said Mike. He swallowed hard. 'Tav, did you give Pete any instructions either from Enzo or from you before the race?'

'No.'

'You sure about that?'

'Yes.'

'You didn't tell him to let me win the race?'

Tavoni looked hard at Mike. 'No. I did not.'

'Did Enzo?'

'Mike, Enzo only speaks through me. You know that.'

'Right.' Mike paused a moment. 'Tav, I'm sorry, but I'm quitting. I can't go on. I'm finished.'

He spotted Duncan entering the bar, seeking him out. It gave him the excuse to go to him, leaving behind a troubled looking Tavoni.

'You alright?' said Duncan. 'You're looking rough.'

'I feel it.' Mike spoke abruptly. 'I should have got his car number changed.'

Duncan stared at him uncomprehendingly. 'What do you mean? Whose…?'

'I thought it read 22. Luigi's at Reims…'

'You're talking about Pete's car?'

'Yeah. I saw Carlotta with some woman, friend of Raymond Mays. She's writing something about driver's deaths connected with their car numbers. She reckons 22's a killer.'

Duncan took a deep breath. It was unnerving to hear Mike talk about it as though it was a normal every day topic of conversation. He came back, reminding him gently. 'Mike, Pete's number was two, not 22.'

'I know that! But I saw it as 22 before the race! The two was doubled up on the front!' Mike screwed up his face in frustration. 'It scared me. So why didn't I warn him?'

Duncan thought of what he could say in reply. He put Mike's crazed suspicions down to the trauma and stress of the day. At any other time he would have laughed and called him a 'complete nutter'.

Mike kept on shaking his head. 'Why didn't I get it changed? Why didn't I?'

'Why didn't you just lock him in his room? I'm not joking Mike. If you really believed it…'

Mike cut in. 'Look, Tav says there were no orders to Pete. There was nothing wrong with the car. I hoped he'd say he'd ordered Pete to let me win. I could have blamed him then. But he didn't. And it's not just the number. He wanted me to overtake. He kept looking in his mirror. He did it on the corner. Peter Lewis told me.'

Duncan looked around hoping Mike's emotions were not written so large that people would notice. He tapped him on the elbow signifying they should leave.

'Come on, let's go.'

'I'm okay.' Mike slumped at an adjacent table which was just vacated. Duncan hesitated then went to the bar. On his return he placed the two glasses of beer on the table and sat down next to Mike. 'You've got to stop beating yourself up,' he said.

Getting no reaction from Mike he pressed on. 'Mike, if somebody's doing me a favour, say he's delivering something to my garage and he gets killed in an accident getting there, it's my fault, is it? That's what you're saying. Pete had an accident Mike. That's all.'

Mike closed his eyes. 'Okay, but makes no difference to that number. I should have stopped him.'

Duncan shushed him and leant forward, pointing a finger. 'Mike. You're not talking about numbers, are you? You're talking about you seeing the future. You'd seen it as 22. So Pete gets killed and it's proof you're a clairvoyant.' His tone was gentle. 'Come on mate.'

Mike screwed up his face, tapping his toe at the floor as if trying to physically fight off the torment. 'Yeah, you're right. I should have locked him in his room, yeah, I should!'

Duncan stood up, picked up both drinks and jerked his head ordering Mike to follow him out of the bar. They went up to his room, Mike still talking. It was not sissy any more to talk about guilt and conscience. He needed help. It did not matter about embarrassing Duncan, not now. He talked about Le Mans and his denial of responsibility for what had happened. Had not the French press blamed him for the deaths and the maimed? He described the panic attacks that had followed and the realisation that they were not expressions of shock but self punishments for that continuing denial. And now, following Pete's death, he was 'in even deeper shit'. The one indisputable fact, he put to Duncan challengingly, was that Pete had died trying to help him win the world championship. How did he get out of that one?

Duncan showed neither embarrassment nor frustration. He spoke in a matter of fact tone. 'Fuck's sake Mike,' he said. 'We've been through all this. Le Mans was an accident. Pete had an accident. Luigi had an accident. Accidents happen. You were just unlucky, that's all. Full stop.'

Mike was having none of it. 'Duncan, if I'd stopped Pete from having that number he'd be alive now.'

Duncan's normal response to such a notion would have been to drag Mike back down to the bar and make him sink a few more pints while taking the piss out of whatever quirk or incident came to the memory. In the pre-swinging 50s the young rugger and motor racing crowd were already letting it all hang out. Boisterousness and laughter were the hallmarks of their breed. They hated having to confront pain and suffering. That had all been left behind in the war. Acknowledging Mike's superstitious fears was not even an option.

'You need to sleep Mike,' he said. 'That's what you need. Got anything for it?'

'Yeah, I have.'

Mike saw that Stuart had come into the room and had been listening to Duncan.

'Do you want a drink Mike?' he said. Then he saw the glasses of beer. 'Oh you've got one.'

'I'll have a brandy.'

Stuart picked up the phone to speak to room service and was surprised to see that Mike was going out.

'You coming back Mike?'

'Yeah.'

Mike went along the corridor and down the stairs to the first floor. Nearby was Louise's room. He stopped outside, uncertain whether to knock or wait.

Louise was inside the room, propped up on the bed, fully dressed. She had done little since arriving back from Bonn, except sit there in a daze. None of Pete's things had been moved, though Beba and Lulu had been wondering about them. Both women had stayed close to Carlotta for hours after her attempted suicide in Reims, spending the time in slowly and carefully packing away her clothes and toiletries. She had ignored them, such was her passion. Shocked yes, but with a groundswell of hatred soon to billow up, soon to take control, pushing away denial and the first symptoms of grief.

Louise, on the other hand, was still firmly fixed in her original state of denial, feeling that someone would come along and state that Pete was still alive, that it was all a dreadful mistake. The evidence lay all around her, didn't it? Pete's wooden puzzle still sat on the dressing table. A truck magazine lay on the top of his bedside cabinet. His toothbrush and razor were still in the bathroom. His clothes were still in the racks next to hers. His striped pyjamas had been lain neatly on the bed by the room maid, the first thing that Louise noticed when she had entered. On the table at his bedside was a photograph that Pete had taken of Mike and herself before the French Grand Prix. It showed her wearing Pete's brown helmet that came down to her nose. Mike stood alongside, leaning backwards and letting out a guffaw.

To her these things were real and tangible, responding to touch and sight. What had happened from the moment that Duncan had approached her in the pits remained a collection of memories without substance – the awful road journey, the white sheet lifting from the body. The reality of the present and the flashes from the past posed a contradiction to each other that she could not untangle.

Beba and Lulu, apart from getting the doctor from the Medical Centre to give Louise a sedative, had done all they could up to that moment. Lulu had taken Pete's suitcase from the bottom of the wardrobe and placed it open on the floor ready for packing, but Louise had stopped her with a 'No', accompanied by a quick cutting motion of the hand. Lulu had ceased immediately and rejoined Beba sitting at the bedside, hoping that Louise would say or do something to which they could respond.

But now, as the alarm clock at Louise's bedside ticked towards 10.35pm, they began to murmur to each other, trying to work out the best way to proceed. Should they start packing away her things, not wait until the morning? And would Louise want to take Pete's clothes with her or leave them behind? Talking to Louise, trying to get her to speak, had been rewarded with little response so far. The sedatives she was taking had not helped in this respect.

Suddenly they were startled as Louise rammed both fists into her lap with a short angry sound, a mixture of grief and self loathing, hating herself for having allowed Pete to take part in such a deadly sport at which common sense shouted out that it was all madness, acts of insanity. She had endured many hours of fear and stress – and for what? The outcome had been what she had dreaded ever since the first race in which she had seen Pete compete.

There came a knock at the door. Lulu went to open it and found Mike outside. She let him straight in without a word.

He stopped at the sight of Louise, then went to sit beside her. She tried a smile but ended up giving a little mewing sound.

Mike knew he would not have long. 'Louise, I'm sorry but I just have to ask you one question.'

She screwed up her face and shook her head quickly.

'Did Pete tell you he was going to help me win the race?'

It defeated her, unable to grasp what he meant.

Mike had to persist. 'Louise. Did he?'

Beba and Lulu glanced anxiously at each other. It was Lulu who spoke quietly and pleadingly. 'Mike…Please.'

'No.' Louise said. Then she repeated it slowly. 'No, he didn't.'

Mike nodded in acceptance. He bent down to kiss her cheek and then left the room. As he went up the stairs back to his room, his head was cast down in anguish and so did not notice Carlotta descending the staircase towards him. As they passed each other she stopped for a moment, about to speak, but decided against it. Her English was minimal, having no means of communicating her confusion. And what could she have said anyway, even in translation?

She wanted to explain that Luigi's death had plunged her into a blind rage with him and Collins for rejecting Luigi's plea. Had not there been a direct connection between his death and their callousness? One followed the other. But now that Collins had died she did not feel any of the gloating pleasure of revenge that she had anticipated.

Instead of the thrill of seeing one of her hated enemies dead, she now felt only fear. She had no recall of the actual English words she had used outside the hotel in Reims, for they were parroted sounds. But she remembered the vindictiveness that she had conveyed in her screaming voice. And she vividly recalled the moment in the cathedral when she had turned to Hawthorn and blown out her candle in his face. Now she was terrified that he, in turn, would die in accordance with her desire.

There was self pity. Was she not a basically decent hard working Catholic girl who had fallen for a married racing driver? She had suffered enough from her family's opprobrium due to that relationship. That, in itself, had been hard enough to bear but what now faced her was beyond fear itself, at least fear of her life on earth. She was already summoning up all her strength to go to confession, but on seeing Hawthorn as a fellow soul in torment she had wanted to stop him and confess it to him in person.

At some point she decided she would do it. And she would go to confession. The latter first.

But then an awful thought occurred to her. What would she actually confess? Had she cursed Collins and Hawthorn to die – or had she merely hoped? She tried hard to remember, but it was useless. She needed to speak to the one person who could save her from damnation. As she entered her room she reminded herself that she only had to ask one question.

\* \* \* \* \*

By midnight the hotel was silent. But time, for those congregated in Mike's room, meant nothing. Stuart, Harry and Duncan were still preoccupied with keeping Mike from tearing himself apart. He had lurched from rage to anguish and back again in the hour after seeing Lewis.

'I could have changed Pete's number. I should have, shouldn't I, because I was terrified! And what was he doing killing himself for me? You can't drive for two people! I wish it had been me. It should have been me. I'll never sit in another fucking race car again!'

They let him ramble on. Gradually his rage diminished and he sat staring at the floor.

It was then that Harry spoke up. He had been waiting for the moment.

'Mike. Please listen.'

Harry spoke calmly and firmly. 'I was a tank commander on D Day plus one. Just think about that day. Ike gave the go-ahead knowing the sea was rough, that casualties would be high. I was lucky. I went a day later on Omaha. I let one of our tanks go in front of me into this road, one of those sunken roads. There was a German Tiger tank there. Fifty yards away facing him, it blew him to kingdom come. I backed and cleared off. I saw my best friend's head blown off Mike. I had years of guilt just from that one thing. Why did I let him go first? Then I started reading the history books. Those guys who bombed Hamburg and Dresden, created fire storms. A hundred thousand dead in one night, all the air sucked out of the cellars they sheltered in, women and kids.'

He paused. 'Mike, you didn't set out to kill anybody. But things happen. And there's bad luck and there's coincidence that means bad luck. That's all it is. Pete got killed doing what he did. You had no control over it, did you?'

He finished to supportive murmurs from Stuart and Duncan.

Mike had listened. But Harry's homily about guilt, that might have helped before Pete's death, was no longer useful. He had gone beyond that. It was no longer the debilitating sense of guilt that tortured his mind, but the knowledge that he should pay back that which he owed. He never had any means of paying back the enormous debt for the suffering he believed he had caused at Le Mans. Neither had he any means of making up for the death of Luigi. But Pete was a different matter. How did you deal with something like that? The one thing that he did know was that he was quitting. There was no doubt about that.

# **Chapter** Eleven

**Monday 4 August 1958**

At 10am Duncan drove Mike and Louise from the Nürburgring heading for Bonn airport. It had been arranged that they would be ushered aboard the London flight ahead of the other passengers. As they walked quickly towards the boarding gate, Mike holding Louise close to him, Duncan parried questions from reporters hurrying alongside, telling them that Mike and Louise were both worn out and needed rest. They would only answer questions on their arrival at Heathrow.

However, the sleep that they secured during the flight on the DC7 was only the best that sedatives can induce and in missing the meal and refreshments it only served to increase their weariness on arrival.

White faced and looking drawn, Mike escorted Louise across the tarmac looked upon by a packed crowd on the overhead observation platform, all eager to get a glimpse of the tragic widow and dejected Golden Boy. Even before they made it to the Press reception, reporters were firing questions at them to the accompaniment of flashing cameras.

Duncan first took the microphone to inform the press pack that Mike would make a statement but that neither he nor Louise would answer questions.

Mike had prepared a two minute speech. In the event it lasted only a few seconds.

'Pete Collins was my best friend,' he bravely announced. 'Louise has lost a wonderful husband that none of us will ever forget. He was the best. He was the most unselfish…'

He broke off, swallowing hard. Realising that his voice was about to crack with emotion he put up the palm of his right hand and with his jaw clenched nodded in affirmation. Then he took Louise's arm, asking if they could be excused as they were both exhausted and they had to face a long drive ahead. Despite his plea a few reporters still chased them into the car park asking questions.

Bill Morgan, the manager of Mike's Tourist Trophy Garage in Farnham, was waiting for them with his car. He handed the car keys to Duncan but Mike intervened. No, he insisted he was going to drive. No amount of protestation and warning would deflect him from his purpose.

It was a mistake. Mike arrived at Kidderminster in such a state that he could not remember the route to Louise and Pete's house and neither could Louise. They were kindly rescued by Alistair Wilson, the generous owner of the Black Boy Hotel in nearby Bewdley. He gave them a room each 'on the house'.

Louise suddenly could not face going into an enclosed space. She had to remain outside seated at a table. Mike brought her out a double brandy and a beer for himself.

After a few sips Louise spoke, hardly daring to look at him.

'Are you going to carry on?' But then she looked at him seriously as if it was important to know.

Mike's first instinct was that she was going to point out his obligation to Pete. It was a thought that had passed through his mind in his confession to Duncan but had then dismissed it. Put simply, if Pete had died helping him to win the race was it not his duty then to carry on, to win the world championships so that Pete's great sacrifice would not have been in vain?

'Do you want me carry on?'

'No Mike. It's crazy.' She tailed off. 'I don't want to see you…'

'No,' he said. 'Don't worry about me. No chance. I'm finished.'

Louise took a deep breath and placed the flat of her hand against her chest. 'Good. I'm glad.' She stretched out an arm to touch his hand.

For the moment they understood each other and no more was said. But, having thought about it, he could not rid himself of the troubling notion. If his troubles were all due to some form of indebtedness should he not try as hard as he could to redeem the one debt that was within his power to make happen? There would never be any chance of redeeming himself over the Le Mans tragedy. But Pete's death – and Luigi's come to that – were his personal responsibility. He asked himself: could he live with Luigi's death? The answer was yes. But Pete's was a different matter altogether as cause and effect were directly linked. He was still mulling over these thoughts until he went to bed, until the moment that he passed out through exhaustion.

The next morning he drove Louise to Shatterford Grange, her home near Kidderminster, where messages of condolence began to arrive from world wide. Louise tried to read them all in between taking telegrams at the door, but then gave up when the next day brought a sackful of mail, a testimony to Pete's popularity. Due to his philanthropic work for local schools and youth clubs the Kidderminster town council flew its flags at half mast.

That evening, as they sat going through the pile of mail, Louise suddenly begged Mike not to stay any longer. She assured him that she was okay, bearing up as anyone could in the circumstances. At his protest she placed a finger on his lips, said she would be fine until her parents arrived overnight from New York.

In a farewell embrace she said they would meet next at the funeral, after which they should, together, plan Pete's memorial service.

* * * * *

Enzo Ferrari was coping better than he anticipated. If anyone had told him that he would lose two drivers in less than a month, that 50 per cent of his driving talent would be gone in only 28 days, he would have said they were *stupido*. Fortunately it was now generally accepted throughout Italy that Luigi Musso's death had been caused by his own fault by allowing his personal problems to affect his driving. But when Enzo had heard the terrible news from Germany he had devoted all his energies to preparing himself for the inevitable relaunch of an attack from church and press that, this time, might be so powerful that he would have no alternative but to withdraw from racing altogether.

Having established every detail of the accident firmly in his mind through Tavoni's diligent reporting he had agreed to be interviewed on film, television and radio on the evening of the tragedy. He hoped that it would create a breathing space ahead of Tavoni's return to Maranello the next day. The message was rammed home. He strongly rebuffed any suggestion that the death of Peter Collins could be attributed in any way to the Scuderia or to the factory that had manufactured his racing car.

In order to ensure global coverage Enzo intended to impress viewers of national television and worldwide cinematic newsreels with a show of emotion for the death of his adopted son. Nevertheless, he would be careful to hold back the tears and not to sound too tragic since the death of his real son could not be seen to be overshadowed by his grief for a foreign driver, no matter how warm their relationship had been.

As it turned out the interviews passed successfully. His answers had been assured and confident, even to the extent of welcoming questions about the car, such was his aplomb. He summed up by declaring it was a case of driver error that no one, he emphasised, could understand or imagine.

He started answering questions by pointing out that Pete's racing car had been passed as race worthy. What Peter Collins had done by not turning into a corner defied logic. Had he survived he would have faced questions that were solely about his state of mind at the time of the accident.

Enzo answered questions about Pete. Could he have suffered from a blackout or stroke? Enzo had foreseen the question and had a doctor on hand who stated that the experts at the Bonn University Clinic had not authorised a full autopsy. There was no need, in their estimation. The doctor produced a medical report on Pete's suitability to drive a racing car and it showed that he was classed as A1, the topmost level on the scale of physical health. As to the actual cause of death, the senior neurologist at the clinic was certain that cause of death was brain damage and a severed spinal cord. These injuries to a young man as fit as Peter Collins hardly argued the case for a post mortem.

On Tavoni's arrival at Enzo's headquarters on the Via Trento Trieste he told Enzo that they had another problem. It was put in a delicate manner. He said that Mike had told him he was retiring. It was understandable. Many drivers, shocked by the deaths of men who had been their friends, frequently announced their retirement from the brutal sport, but most were back within weeks.

As Enzo listened to Tavoni his eyes softened and he allowed himself a thin reflective smile. The passion for motor racing, once it entered the blood became a drug and could turn the driver into an addict. He knew it to be true as he had been one himself. He had been one of the lucky ones. He had survived.

When Tavoni had finished briefing him, he took off his black spectacles, ran a hand over his forehead and sat back.

'Yes', he said. 'But we must make sure Mike drives in Portugal. I have lost one possible world champion, two if you count Luigi. I can't afford to lose a third. Who is the best person to talk with him, to make him feel easier?'

Tavoni thought for a moment. 'I would say that Louise is the one. She is very close to Mike.'

'But she will be stricken. Is it wise?'

'It depends on how you approach her, I suppose,' said Tavoni.

'Good. I'll contact her. In the meantime, plan for Portugal. Hawthorn must be there.'

'You want me to start preparing Mike's car tomorrow or wait?'

'Prepare it now,' replied Enzo. 'You have 16 days.'

'No, you mean 13. He must be there for the practice sessions.'

Enzo nodded his head. 'Yes. He will be.'

'I wish I had your certainty.'

'I will deal with it. Don't worry.'

Enzo looked firmly into Tavoni's eyes.

*　*　*　*　*

Winifred Hawthorn was as relieved by Pete's death as she was shocked. Mike had telephoned her shortly after the race to tell her to worry no more. He would never sit in another racing car he declared. He was adamant about it.

'Thank God,' was her spoken reaction. 'Oh thank God.' She had then started to weep.

On Tuesday 6 August Mike arrived back from Shatterford to give his mother a special hug for putting up with him all those years. It was now all over and they were never to talk about it again, he said.

Winifred hugged him back and cried for Pete and Louise.

Later that evening, Mike drove over to join Duncan at The Barley Mow.

The air was still warm after the heat of the day and they sat outside in the pub garden reminiscing about the 'old days' of driving road cars in timed dashes. Mike recalled his motorcycle escapades while serving as an apprentice at a local engineering firm at the same time as he attended Guildford Technical College. They chuckled easily at some of the stories.

Mike became gung ho as he went back to his teens. 'I was 18. There were three of us. It was all boozing and birds.' 'Sorry,' he corrected himself. 'Bikes, boozing and birds. I had a 250cc Triumph, won two cups in Novice Trials. We used to go pub crawling. We'd start at The Bush in Farnham and end up here. Great days. Yeah…'

'Then you met me and all your troubles started.' Duncan gave a laugh. He was pleased to find that Mike was also laughing.

'Yeah, then dad bought me a Fiat 500. Top speed 65 miles an hour. I kept burning out the exhaust valves. He used to have a fit.'

Mike chuckled to himself in remembrance but then noticed that Duncan was not listening to him, his half turned head suggesting he was listening instead to a strong male voice coming from a table behind him. The man in question was a young soldier in uniform holding forth to an audience of two attractive looking girls, both clutching glasses of Babycham.

Mike frowned because at that moment the squaddie glanced at him as he talked, as though he was the subject of his discourse. It was on his second glance that he caught Mike's stare. It caused him to break off to raise his glass to him with a grin.

'I don't know how you did it, but you were smarter than me.'

'How do you mean?' said Mike.

'Smarter than most of us. But you'd got the money. Money talks, eh?'

Duncan wanted to stop the confrontation there and then but Mike was ahead of him, already on his feet. 'What do you mean by that?'

The soldier grinned. 'You know what I mean,' he said leeringly.

'No I don't. Go on, what is it?' Mike's blood was up and Duncan's raised arm was ignored as he took a step closer to the squaddie.

The soldier had lost his grin. 'I mean you got out of National Service. Be honest. You was a cheat, gallivanting off, having fun driving racing cars while us poor bastards…'

He got no further because Mike swung his arm and socked him on the nose. The soldier shouted out in pain, blood splashing on the table. It drew a scream from one of the girls.

Duncan whisked Mike out of the garden and into the car park.

'Mike, fuck's sake! It'll get in all the papers. The police will be round. Jesus.'

'Doesn't matter,' said Mike. 'I'm nobody now. They can take away my racing licence. They can fine me. Let them. I don't care.'

\* \* \* \* \*

Carlotta had trouble contacting the English speaking barman at The Grand Hotel du Nord in Reims. She had forgotten his name but when she finally got through to him his first reaction was to go on the alert, her voice bringing him uncomfortably back to the off duty drink that he had shared with her on the evening of the French Grand Prix, especially the subject of their conversation. It was not something he would forget in a hurry.

She had come to him offering a tip in exchange for an English phrase, something with which to communicate her visceral loathing of Hawthorn and Collins, even to the extent of issuing them with a *maledizione*, or 'curse'. When he had heard subsequently of the death of Peter Collins a hot flush had run through his body from guilt and fear. And now she was asking him what he had taught her to say, thereby implying he was complicit in her original intent. It made him highly nervous.

In his hesitation Carlotta pitched in again, her impatient voice turning the request into an insistent demand. 'Come on. What did I say? "I curse you to die" or "I hope you die"? Come on, tell me!'

His heart thumped. Was the call being tape recorded? He was young and innocent enough to worry that what he had taught her to say might, in some countries, be construed as criminal. He wished now that he had not taken her money. Could it be used to point the finger at him as having entered into some form of contract with her?

He had felt concerned enough at the time, but had only got her verbal promise that what she proposed to do would not be held against him. He should have got it in writing. Another thought brought beads of sweat to his forehead. Had she been interviewed by the police? Was that why she was calling him, to pin the blame on him? He put the suggestion to her, abruptly.

She was offended, horrified. Of course not. It was a matter of conscience. What she had done was terrible – if she had done it. She demanded to know the exact words he had given her. She gave him her word on her mother's grave that he would not suffer in any way. But tell her he must. And now, immediately.

Partially convinced of her sincerity he gave her the answer she hoped for.

Instead of 'I curse you to die' she had been given 'I hope you die'.

The barman then stammered out an excuse that he was needed in the hotel. After that the line went dead.

Carlotta was at first relieved. She could now go to confession and say as many 'Hail Marys' in penance as ordered, her sins washed away. But then she recalled that the sentence in Italian she had wanted translated was not 'I hope' but 'I curse you to die'. Had he just now been afraid to give it to her and had changed it to 'I hope'? All she knew was that he had answered her phone call in a jumpy state and could have said anything to get rid of her. In her mounting dread came another fearful thought. There was still Hawthorn. He had been included in the curse. She had included him in her condemnation, hadn't she? It seemed to her there was no escape from her conscience.

Carlotta had been born into a family of 12 children in Calabria, a southern part of Italy, where poverty was the norm and scratching a living from the bleak and windswept interior was all that was on offer. She had been a feisty 18-year-old when introduced to the superstitious practices that had been passed down by generations of women from mediaeval times. The outstanding ritual was the curse of the *Malocchio* or 'Evil Eye'. In essence it was deployed as a protection from masculine threats, menaces and physical brutality, even rape. Her grandmother had shown her what to do if ever she feared that she had cursed someone in haste and needed revoking. A sure way of divining its power or its failure was to drip olive oil into a plate of water. If it formed one large drop it was a sure sign that the curse had been given and was ongoing.

Carlotta took a bottle of Virgin olive oil, took out the cork and poured a little of the golden fluid into a saucer of water. Breathing hard, her palms sweating, she kneeled down to close her eyes and chant the prayers that only women were allowed to know.

She then opened her eyes and stared at the plate. The oil had broken up into droplets and had spread out. The curse was broken and she was whole again.

\* \* \* \* \*

If Carlotta had known that Mike had already decided to quit motor racing she would have thought her prayer had been successful. If she could have seen him walking into Guy's Hospital and known why he was there she would have also prayed for his recovery. Because he was in pain.

This time Duncan accompanied him. They walked from the car park through the flapping double doors into the main corridor and turned right at the 'Urology' department sign. The consultant was late, but the nursing sister, as always respectful of Mike's fame, ushered them into a private room.

It was a different consultant who eventually 'got round' to seeing Mike, a man who had no time for motor racing and showed it. His first act was to give Mike a morphine jab.

'I can't understand it,' he said looking at Mike's notes. 'You continue to drive these things but...'

'Not any longer,' Mike interrupted. 'I've retired.'

'Oh. Good. About time too.'

After examining him the consultant told Mike to 'rest as much as possible', gave him some more painkillers and said his goodbye.

On the journey home Mike was happy about one thing. 'Glad I didn't tell him about Taffy's painkillers else he'd have confiscated them, the bastard.'

He grinned at his own black humour. He was pretty sure that the consultant knew he had a limited life span without actually telling him such. Had there not been a sense of finality in his farewell? Suddenly, without any hint of embarrassment, he told Duncan that he could not ignore Pete's death, that there was no doubt that he had 'got the chop' looking out for him in his mirrors.

That evening Duncan telephoned Stuart to ask him a question. Why, did he think, had Mike not announced his retirement publicly?

'He's not decided. It's obvious,' said Stuart.

'That's what I think.'

Stuart said – and Duncan agreed – that Mike was trapped. He felt that he should go on to win the world championship to help remove Pete's death from his conscience, but he could not continue to ignore the medical warnings. Of all dilemmas it was classic.

'What do you think we can do?' said Duncan. 'How do we get him sorted?'

They spent the next half hour discussing and working out possible scenarios that were variations on the main theme, all designed to make it easier for Mike, whatever the outcome. Duncan, valuing Stuart's sincerity and keen mind but unsure that he was doing the right thing, asked him if he would present the package to Mike when all three, hopefully, would meet at The Barley Mow that evening.

Stuart was only too pleased. To him, the eternal outcast from the macho world, to be invited by the big man to share the intimacies involved in sorting out The Golden Boy's Achilles Heel did as much for his ego as winning the Grand Prix.

Duncan was unsure how Mike would react to Stuart's presence but nevertheless went ahead in ringing him after his conversation with Stuart. The meeting was confirmed for that evening.

Stuart brought with him a copy of the *Daily Express* that ran the story of the Pope's appeal to Enzo Ferrari asking him 'to stop the slaughter'. Mike read the first couple of paragraphs and merely shrugged.

'Enzo won't pack it in. He's been there before,' was his dry comment.

Duncan looked at Stuart who nodded, paused a little and then launched into outlining the choices that they believed were open to Mike. He put the points succinctly and precisely. The best possible outcome, he said, was that Enzo obeyed the Pope's plea to withdraw from motor racing. If that happened Mike would be automatically retired.

He could also announce that he had intended to retire at the end of the season in order to concentrate on his family business. Thus there would be no stigma attached to his retirement and thus no public blame. His millions of fans would have no choice but to accept it, would have no option but express their sorrow that he had been cut off in his title bid.

There was another opportunity given this eventuality, added Stuart. 'As soon as Ferrari announces he's quitting you can tell the press that you failed your army medical. You'll show you did nothing selfish or unpatriotic to escape National Service. It won't matter losing your racing licence then because you wouldn't be racing any more. And don't forget it would put paid to all that malicious gossip about you in the press. The least they could do is apologise.'

Mike nodded.

'And there's one more thing.' Stuart looked Mike directly in the eye. 'We know you feel bad about Pete. You think you owe him a big debt...'

'No, I do owe him a big debt. Massive.'

Stuart flickered a little, but stuck to his ground.

'Yes,' he said. 'That's the point. You couldn't repay it by harming yourself any more. You'd have the means taken away.'

'What if Enzo doesn't quit?' Mike was getting a little irritated at Stuart lecturing him about his personal feelings.

Duncan sensed it and took over from Stuart. 'Mike, we discussed it. Stuart worked out the averages over the races this year. If Enzo doesn't quit but you do, you could still end up as world champion.' He glanced at Stuart. 'Tell him, go on.'

Stuart took a deep breath. 'I'm not doing Stirling down now. He is my teammate, but…'

'You're going to puncture his tyres,' said Mike dryly.

Duncan laughed but Stuart was concerned that he made his point. 'No Mike. No need. I'm talking about statistics. There are three races left. On past performances Stirling has a 'better than evens' chance of winning the Portuguese, but he'll probably have his engine break down or blow up in Italy and he'd be placed third in the last race in Morocco.'

'On how many races have you worked that out?' said Mike. 'That's rubbish. I…'

'No Mike', Duncan butted in, anxious to save Stuart from being embarrassed. 'It isn't. Because Stuart was going to add one more thing, weren't you?'

'Yes,' said Stuart. 'If Enzo doesn't quit you might do one more race, the Portuguese. It depends on how you are. How you feel. What the doctors say. You'd have to decide. You'd have to hope you'd do well there, stop Stirling gaining points. But then you'd only miss two races.'

There was a pause as Mike continued to look at Stuart while thinking about it.

'Mike,' said Duncan firmly. 'The next race after Portugal is Monza and you wouldn't want to do that again, would you?' He raised his eyebrows. 'Those high curves, the banks? The Monza 500?'

Mike nodded, looking into his beer. 'No. Okay Stuart, have you worked out how many points I'd beat Stirling by at the end?'

'If you stop now, no more than one. If you did the Portuguese then the statistics would get better. I know it's all a gamble but it's the best we can do.'

Mike thought about it some more and had to admit to himself that his two friends had eased his dilemma.

'Thanks fellers,' he said. 'I appreciate it. Thanks a lot. I've got to think.'

Mike took a drink of beer as Duncan and Stuart waited for him to come to a decision.

His first was easy to make. He decided that he would do what Stuart had suggested, retire as soon as Enzo withdrew from Grand Prix. But then what? As for the future?

He looked into the faces of Duncan and Stuart who awaited his decision. He took another thoughtful sip of beer. He wanted to live a normal life, hopefully go into the car business with Duncan. He did not want to end up a physical wreck unable to enjoy that life. He looked up and smiled at Stuart's hopeful expression.

'Yeah, okay.'

'What? You'll do what?' said Duncan, with a quick exchange of glances with Stuart.

'I'll do one more.' Mike grinned, roughly rubbed Stuart's hair and poked Duncan in the chest. 'You two…who needs friends?'

But if they thought their work was done and dusted, Duncan and Stuart were in for a shock.

* * * * *

On Mike's return home he found Winifred in the room that his father had converted into an office and where Mike kept some of his memorabilia. He caught her holding one of his prize cups.

'I'm putting these away Mike…' she faltered. But then seemed to draw strength. 'I don't want you to have to look at them and…' She weakened again, put the cup down to run a finger beneath her wet eye. 'And I don't want to see them anymore either.'

As she broke down and continued to sob Mike looked on in dismay. In the meeting with Duncan and Stuart he had forgotten about his mother. Could he put her through the agony of one more race? He embraced her.

'It's okay mum,' he whispered. 'I told you I'd finished.'

She drew back to look into his face. 'You really mean that?'

'Yes, I said so.'

Winifred nodded. 'So when will you announce it?'

Mike was considering his reply when the telephone rang. Mike went into the hallway to pick up the receiver. It was Louise saying that she had received a letter from Enzo inviting her to Maranello. 'I said I'd go after the funeral. He wants to present me with something. To honour Pete. The press are going to be there. He was so insistent. I did promise. Will you come with me?'

'Has he said anything else?? said Mike. 'Nothing about quitting?'

'No.' Louise said. 'How's Winifred?'

Mike glanced towards the kitchen where Winifred had gone to prepare supper. He agonised, then hedged his bets.

'I was going to wait for Enzo to pack it in,' he said. 'Tell you what. If he doesn't I will at Maranello. I'll give the old man a shock. You never know, he might even honour me as well.'

She laughed along with him. After they said their goodbyes, he put down the receiver and hoped that in the days running up to their flight to Italy that news would come out of Maranello that would please his friends, his mother and keep him living for as long as possible.

# **Chapter** Twelve

The body of Peter Collins was flown from Germany to Heathrow and taken by road to St Mary's Church in Stone, Staffordshire, a small market town seven miles north of Stafford where, on the eve of the funeral, it was placed in front of the altar. A vigil service was held overnight.

Pete's parents, having decided that the funeral service would be a strictly family affair with a few invited friends, had informed Louise of their decision by telephone. She had detected a guarded tone in Pat Collins's voice and wondered why.

The following morning, Thursday 14 August, promised sunshine and showers in quick succession. The weather's vicissitude matched Louise's mood when she chanced to open two letters from the large pile that had accumulated over the week. The first was warm and heartening, from a Bishop Fyffe whose house Louise and Peter had been in the process of buying. Enclosed was a cheque for the large deposit that they had paid to the Bishop's solicitor only 12 days before. Such uncalled for benevolence touched Louise as the contract had been signed by both parties. Despite Pete's death she believed that she was still morally, even if not legally, bound to purchase.

However, by a bizarre coincidence the very next letter she opened was from Pat Collins and was in no way heartening. It contained a stamped addressed envelope bearing his address. Inside was a typewritten statement with a few dots in a line at the bottom with Louise's name printed beneath, indicating where she should sign. It read:

'I, Louise Collins, hereby renounce any rights that I may have acquired by marriage to my deceased husband's share in the business of Kidderminster Motors Ltd.'

The accompanying note pointed out that as she was 'a star of the American theatre' she did not have to worry about 'earning her living'.

Louise immediately burst into tears, not because she had expected to share in the family business but because of the hard nosed insensitive act of the businessman, especially on the day of the funeral. She was fortunate that her own father, Andrew Cordier, was there to comfort her. He had brought with him a letter of condolences from the General Secretary of the United Nations, Dag Hammarskjold. Although Andrew had been scheduled to assist with an emergency meeting dealing with the ongoing tense situation in Lebanon and Jordan the General Secretary had insisted that his daughter's bereavement should come before his part in the solving of problems, however urgent, in the Middle East.

Mike, who had stayed overnight at the Black Boy Hotel, woke to the prospect of another day of depression and anxiety. He was dreading the funeral service, having suffered a panic attack during that of Luigi Musso. His other fear was that Carlotta might appear in her black widow's garb and cause a disturbance. This was by no means the workings of a paranoid mind. His fear was understandable. If she had travelled to Monaco in order to stalk him why not nip over to Stone Church in Staffordshire? Was it not a reasonably good bet that she would wish to enjoy the *schadenfreude* of seeing the pain of those saying farewell to the man who had 'killed' her lover? Just before Mike left for the church he took the precaution of taking one of his sedative tablets.

Duncan, who had been briefed by Mike on Carlotta's wiles, although not invited to the funeral himself, promised to arrive early as a bodyguard. Should she appear he would do his best to ensure that she would not gain entry to the church, though how he intended to carry out his promise without attracting attention remained to be seen.

Mike arrived at the church, having walked past hundreds of townspeople lining the road. He entered to the muted tones of the organ playing a piece from Purcell and sat next to Louise and her father on the front left side of the nave. It had been expected that she would sit on the right side with Pat and Elaine Collins, but at the last moment could not bring herself to join them.

'I am the Resurrection and the Life...'

As the coffin was carried into church Mike could not help but shed tears. Louise, summoning up all her actress's power of concentration, wept a little with him and then felt remorse when she glanced across the aisle to see Pat and Elaine Collins hugging each other. Money, wealth, concepts of fairness, insensitivity – whatever – the presence of a loved one's death had levelled them all as equals.

At the close of the service Mike and Louise inspected the mass of wreaths that had been placed around the coffin and which stretched into the transept on either side. There were nearly 200, including those from Enzo Ferrari, Juan Fangio, Stirling Moss, Tony Brooks and Tony Vandervell on behalf of the Vanwall team. Afterwards the body was taken to Wolverhampton for cremation. The ashes would then be brought back to Stone and buried in the churchyard.

* * * * *

Louise's father left for New York the next day and Mike took her for lunch at The Black Boy, over which they intended to discuss the format for Pete's Memorial Service.

Instead they found themselves talking about Enzo's invitation. Louise was unsure now whether to accept or not, having heard of his reputation with women.

'Well you are going,' Mike said. 'Because he's invited me as well. I got his letter this morning. I'm going to chaperone you. I can't let you go there on your own.'

'Oh that's so good Mike.' Louise was relieved. 'I was worrying about it. All those stories about him.'

'And nothing about me, the wolf in chaperone's clothing?'

He chuckled as he ate, but then stopped as he saw her face and realised his mistake. He tried to cover up. 'I mean how do I get a taxi in Italy without a beautiful bird?'

The joke fell as heavily as the first. In order to cover up his embarrassment Mike had to keep talking. 'You know what they call Enzo? The old fox. He never does anything if it's not for his good. There'll be something behind getting us to Maranello, you can bet your bottom dollar.'

Louise appeared unaffected. 'Doesn't he want you there to persuade you to carry on? You're his next world champion. And there's only three races left. Most people in the UK want you to go on, don't they?' Louise put a hand to her mouth. 'Oh I'm sorry, I shouldn't have said that. I don't want you to go on. Please believe me. It's just that I'm scared all the time.' She touched his arm. 'But I will try to be there for you if you carry on. I won't like it, but I'll try.' She hesitated. 'Pete told me – about your…'

'Plumbing?'

'I'm sorry?'

'No. He was wrong. Always fussing. I'm okay. Scouts honour.' He picked up the menu. 'Are actresses allowed ice cream?'

Afterwards, they walked down to the riverside and turned right to approach the Bewdley Rowing Club house. He noticed Louise take out a handkerchief and dab the corner of her eye. 'You alright?'

'I keep thinking he's going to call or walk through the door, Mike.'

'So do I.' Mike swallowed hard. 'Bit of a bugger.'

'Yes.' She tried to laugh. It was the way he had said it.

She stuffed the handkerchief up her sleeve. 'I'll tell you what I'm dreading, Enzo inviting me into his shrine. Pete told me about it. His son's photo's there as well as Luigi's. You have to pray with him. I think it's horrible.'

He had tears in his eyes and his voice broke. 'I miss him Louise,' then suddenly, 'I'm sorry…'

'No, don't be.' Louise nodded, biting her lip. She came to him and raised her arms to embrace him. 'What was it you said – "If you were a woman I'd have married you"?'

'Yeah.'

'That would have been an interesting threesome?'

Mike grinned. 'Yeah, it would.' He put a soft hand to the side of her head and she felt its warmth. She knew he would make a pass. With Pete always around, she had never thought of Mike wanting her. But now she would not be surprised. She did not want it to happen. She gathered herself, putting her head back to look at him, smiling bravely. 'Mike, I will be going home after the Service. I'm going back to acting. It's the best form of escape, being other people. Does it make sense?'

'Oh – you mean for good.'

'Yes.' She lowered her arms. 'I've got to.'

'Right.' He let go of her to watch a young man in a racing skiff power his way towards them. He looked back at her. 'Right.'

'That's where my work is.' She absorbed his disappointment, but suddenly remembered. 'Oh! But if you do carry on I promise I'll be there if I'm free. Not just for you, for me as well. I was more scared away from the track than being there. It will be the same with you.'

'You know that Pete never was,' Mike said. 'Not once.'

'I know. That's what made it worse.'

The rower passed them, the water spinning in his wake. Mike watched him go, reflecting on an image of sporting innocence without fear. 'That's what I should have done,' he said. 'The best kind of track, from the boat house to the pub.'

They laughed a little and carried on walking. He frowned. 'I've got this eulogy to read out at the Memorial Service. How do I stop cracking up Louise?'

'When you're reading it why don't you just to think of the good times? Just concentrate on a picture in your mind of how it was.'

'Yeah.' He looked at her. 'Thanks. I'll try and do that.'

They walked on.

'I saw *Some Like it Hot*, did I tell you?' he said.

'No. Did you like it?'

'Yeah. Were you jealous that Marilyn Monroe got your part?'

'Yes. Of course. But I didn't let it hurt too much.'

\* \* \* \* \*

Enzo Ferrari was a commanding figure in whatever company he chose. During World War Two he had played the hard working apolitical manufacturer who successfully dealt with visits from the Gestapo or army patrols operating under the Nazi occupation of Italy. They would drop in without warning to inspect his premises for evidence that might show him as a supplier of weapons or sabotage equipment to the Resistance fighters.

The Germans never discovered that this was, in fact, a real sideline of the factory output in the latter years of the conflict. Enzo was never caught out because of his skilful planning of situations and his ability to control people. Having a natural cunning, allied to an overbearing self confidence, made for the ideal saboteur.

On this warm, but rainy day, in August 1958, he intended to display these talents in dealing with Mike Hawthorn who, Tavoni had assured him, was quitting Ferrari.

It was out of the question, something that Enzo could not possibly accept. He planned an operation to ensure that Mike was kept, literally, on track for the world championship.

At 1.30pm he despatched a car to pick up Louise and Mike from the Bologna train arriving at Modena railway station, due in at 2pm. The train was punctual and they were swiftly brought back to the Via Trento Trieste where Enzo's first act was to embrace Louise.

Speaking through a fiercely loyal interpreter – a trim, tight-lipped woman who would never breach his confidence – he confessed his admiration for her fortitude and offered her *grande commiserazione* for her loss. While making rounded gestures with his hands he declared that Peter had been a wonderful son to himself and Laura. He assured her that he would do everything he could to help her through her trying time. He was *effusivo* in that commitment.

He then turned to clasp Mike's hand in welcome. Still maintaining his grip, he dropped his voice to say in sepulchral tones that he had shaken Peter's hand 'only a week' before his death, during which he had felt 'a troubling sadness'.

Louise, standing next to Mike, heard the translation. She gave a sharp intake of breath.

Mike glanced down at Enzo's hand still gripping his own. 'Do you feel the same way now?' he said. There was a trace of contempt in his voice.

Enzo looked at the interpreter who mistook Mike's meaning and translated it as 'Do you still feel Peter's hand?' No, no. The Commendatore was adamant. Peter was dead. He never had dealings with the after life. Seeing Louise's confusion he bestowed a kiss on her forehead saying that 'Peter was at rest and that God had made him welcome in heaven'. He placed an arm around her shoulders, his moment to invite them both into the shrine room, the moment Louise had feared.

She looked at Mike as if for help, but Enzo was already gently pressurising her arm in the direction of the open door. Short of creating a scene she had no choice but to acquiesce. They entered the room to stand, awkwardly, before the shrine. The perfume from an incense stick was strong.

The framed photographs of Dino and Luigi had been moved to accommodate that of Pete so as to form a balanced trio above and behind the trio of burning candles. Dino's photograph was the largest in the centre. Flowers decorated the base of the shrine. Enzo crossed himself and intoned his usual prayers for the dead. A tear trickled down his cheek.

Louise fumbled to grasp Mike's hand for security. He stared at Pete's photograph, still angry at Enzo's claim to have foreseen his death. But then it begged the question: if it had been written that Pete would die on a certain date it would have happened anyway, so why should he feel guilty? But the spurious notion that beset him on occasions – being a plaything of the gods – he soon dismissed. It was obvious that Enzo made things up. The claim would have been invented. It would turn out to be an opening gambit in a game that was, as yet, unclear.

Mike loathed the sweet smell of incense. It reminded him of Luigi's funeral. His feeling of unease made him close his eyes in an attempt to think of something else in the hope that he might drive it away, but all he could think of was a childhood day in Farnham when he quickly crossed the road rather than walk by a house where someone had died. In the still prevalent Victorian tradition of the 1930s it was common practice for the mourning to draw the curtains of the front room – the best room, one reserved for special occasions – wherein would lie the coffin until the day of the funeral. Even when he had crossed the road he held his breath until he was level with the next house to that of the deceased. Later, after his father had died in a road accident, he told Winifred that he would not be able to stay in the house if his body was kept there.

Luckily, the undertakers had been instructed to take the corpse from the hospital to their own premises where it would remain until the funeral. He need not have worried as, unknown to him at the time, his mother had no more room for his body in the house than she had for him in his later life. There were to be no horses adorned with black plumes, no darkly rich, sweet atmosphere – as in here…

Mike opened his eyes and stared at the deep purple ribbon draped around Dino's photograph. He recalled seeing the same colour in the cathedral. At that point his breathing began to labour, instinct telling him that he was only a few seconds away from reaching the point of critical mass. With his lungs refusing to take in more desperately needed air, he tore himself away and hurried back into the office where he gasped the word 'toilet' to the interpreter. Astonished, she pointed the way and watched him go with his pale face and gaping mouth. Once inside Mike wrenched the brown paper bag from his pocket.

Minutes later, having stabilised his breathing, his brain no longer spinning in free fall, he returned to find Enzo and Louise back in the office and coffee being served. He quickly apologised, said he had felt momentarily sick, but was fine now.

'Molto bene. Molto bene.' Enzo nodded in satisfaction and understanding. He put the tips of his fingers together and paused a moment, then sat upright.

'Michael,' he said grandly, with an imperious tilt of his head – he only used Mike's proper name when he had something big to impart – 'I must tell you that I am going back to the race track. At Monza.' He paused for effect. 'But only if Louise will join me. I want her to be there because Peter's heart was there. It will be a fitting occasion to celebrate his life and success. I hope you agree?'

Mike was stunned. Enzo had not referred to him, either as a companion of Louise at the race track or as driver. Was it possible that Tavoni had actually managed to persuade him that he was sincere in his determination to quit? But if that was the case, why had he been brought there? Mike believed that the sly fox must be driven by some ulterior motive. But what?

He resisted the impulse to ask if Enzo accepted that he was finished with motor racing. Instead he decided to wait and see how it all played out. If the moment came when Enzo's intentions were clear then he would strike back with his declaration of retirement, thus giving the old man no time to deploy any counter ruse.

Until now Mike's knowledge of Enzo had come from test sessions at the Modena circuit. It was there, at the trackside, that he showed an entirely different personality to that in the office. In the pits or paddock the

Commendatore would do nothing but concentrate on the car and its engine in order to extract from them their optimum performance. In that environment he never indulged in grandiose statements or spoke of matters of the spirit. There he was the commander of a team, instructing Tavoni and his mechanics in the esoteric art of 'setting up' the car. In the pursuit of this he absorbed information and processed it like lightning. Not a moment was wasted.

Away from the track it was different. There, other considerations operated. The trouble that people had in dealing with Enzo was that it was his nature to exploit anything of complexity. Instead of unravelling the knot he could so easily twist it to his advantage.

He sipped his coffee and considered how the day was proceeding. So far he was disappointed at Louise's reaction before the shrine, having expected her to break down so that he could hug and console her and – possibly at a later date – seduce. It was a pity that Mike had to be invited, but since he was the target of the operation he had no choice. It annoyed him that the first stage of his aim, the creation of a bond of unity out of a feeling of obligation to the deceased, had failed because of Mike's hurried departure from the shrine. Hah well, he still had them both together for the climax of the afternoon. That was what mattered.

He felt confident that Louise would accept that her husband's memory was best served by Mike carrying on to take the world championship. For Enzo that success would reinforce the marque of Ferrari as a name synonymous with speed and excellence, doing more for his road car manufacturing business than any advertising. Mike, however notable a figure, was of secondary importance to that end. It would be an insular achievement if he became the first British world motor racing champion, whereas Ferrari's would be global.

Enzo lit a cigar as he considered the next stage of his plan. For this he needed the tragic and heroic widow to show how her grief had turned to pride at her beloved husband's best friend setting out to win the coveted laurel wreath in his memory. He had no inkling that his plan was very close to reality, that his proposed suggestion of indebtedness was the very feeling that had plagued Mike in varying degrees since Pete's death. Enzo had never experienced guilt following the death of any one of his racing drivers. Unlike Mike, Enzo had never felt the need to pay back a life debt in such a situation. Such ideas were anathema to Enzo's moral philosophy and would so remain until the day he died.

\* \* \* \* \*

It was 4pm and time for the piece de resistance of the day. Enzo was taking them to the factory, he said. There was something there that 'they ought to see'.

Mike and Louise allowed themselves to be escorted outside where Enzo's car was waiting. The interpreter sat in the front passenger seat, Louise and Mike in the rear.

During the brief journey Mike noticed that Enzo glanced at his watch a couple of times. Shortly afterwards the car turned off the road and into an open space, beyond which stood a large brick building with a square portal beneath. Over the opening the Ferrari name was emblazoned in yellow.

Enzo drove through the opening to park outside the main manufacturing and assembly workshops. As they left the car Mike and Louise were struck by the silence of the place. It could have been a Sunday morning. The large factory doors were shut and no one as yet had come out of the entrance door to welcome them. They noticed that there was no sign of life either in the adjoining buildings that housed the other departments.

Louise exchanged nervous glances with Mike. Enzo, unable to resist a smug smile at her concern, escorted them through the entrance and into the racing car department – and all without a word being spoken.

As they entered the engine workshop a wall of blinding lights popped at them, accompanied by the sound of enthusiastic applause. Mike and Louise found themselves confronting the Ferrari workforce, four ranks of engineers dressed in immaculate blue uniforms, standing in two lines in the form of a vee, each line running parallel with mounted engines in various states of construction. The steel built workshop was painted in an immaculate white. The floor was pristine. The normal factory ambience was softened by groups of large green shrubs placed alongside its walls and illuminated by wall lights.

Mike could not help smiling. If he had been with Duncan they would have rocked with cynical laughter. It was lamentably obvious why Enzo had invited him to Maranello, to trap him, to make it impossible to declare his retirement. And Louise was there for her photograph to appear in the national press showing her bravery in making the journey in support of Pete's best friend, a hero who carried the flag for Britain. The Ferrari employees were present en force as photo fodder for Enzo's 'promotion'. Mike even thought that the photographs could even appear in the English papers the following morning giving him no time to kill the story with his denial.

Mike did not have long to wait for confirmation. It came when Enzo raised his hand to stem the applause. As it died down he addressed his audience. 'Miei amici benvenuti a Mike e Louise,' he said.

After the interpreter had translated the welcome he took Louise's arm to speak of her tragic loss, reminding them that it was much greater than his own, despite having loved Pete as 'his favourite son'. He then spoke of his tradition of not attending races in recent years. It was something he intended to break, but only if Louise were gracious enough to accompany him. He announced that he would be at Monza for the Italian Grand Prix and hopefully Louise would be there to dedicate the race to the memory of her beloved husband as well as see Mike win it.

'And Peter will be there helping him in spirit,' he added.

Before Louise could utter any reaction he stepped in front of her, placed a hand on Mike's shoulder and delivered his coup de grace. 'Questo è Michael e diventerà il primo motore di mondo British racing campione.'

Mike needed no translation when he heard the final three words. 'The bastard,' he thought. 'The cunning bastard.' He now saw the captions over the photographs.

'Tragic widow backs Mike'. 'Mike to win it for Pete.' The Italian press, of course, would have 'Tragic widow backs Ferrari'.

Enzo's speech was greeted with another outburst of applause. His hand remained on Mike's shoulder.

And how do you dig yourself out of that one? Mike looked at Louise. She had shrunk within, her face set in stone. Mike made an instinctive movement of his shoulders, encouraging Enzo to remove his hand. Should he strike back now? Was this the time to call Enzo a fraud in front of the assembled workforce as well as the press? He could not. The bastard had ambushed him, making it impossible.

Worse, Enzo was using them as pawns in his power game, having brought them all the way to Italy without any thought as to Louise's stress and misery in bereavement. What particularly galled Mike was that Enzo must have been aware that his two victims, if not knowing beforehand, must now be aware that they were his victims. Or was he so taken in by his own pomp that he had not even given it a thought? Maybe racing drivers and actresses, in his book, were dense creatures equipped with primitive brains. Even if he had known how they must have felt it was plainly obvious that he cared not a jot for the contempt that they must have felt. Mike decided that, as soon as he arrived home, he would make contact with someone he knew in Reuters news agency, declare his immediate retirement and hope that the news would be out before the story broke from Maranello. It was a long shot since Enzo probably would have foreseen that possibility and ensured that the story and photographs would be out before he had that opportunity. In that case he would stick two fingers up to him, give news of his retirement and let the bastard try and extricate himself from his own mess.

Enzo gave a signal. A door to an office opened and out stepped the tiny daughter of one of the employees carrying a large bouquet of flowers which she presented to Louise. It was the signal for another outbreak of applause.

It was then that Mike realised that Tavoni was absent and knew the reason. Knowing that Mike had told him he was retiring Enzo had never intended his team manager to be part of the welcoming party, knowing he would be too embarrassed by it all. Enzo patently cared more for Tavoni's sensitivity than theirs.

Back at the Ferrari office Mike shook Enzo's hand for the last time and saw in his dark searching eyes a spark of triumph.

'Thank God,' sighed Louise as they settled down in the compartment of the train taking them to Bologna where they would spend the night before flying home the next day.

She said she had to admire Enzo's acting talent. 'He should get an Academy Award. He wants everybody to feel they owe him something.' Then, suddenly in concern, she said, 'Mike, tell me seriously. Are you going to do what he wants?'

'Are you?' said Mike.

Louise sat back. 'I don't want to, no. It depends on you. He didn't leave you with much choice, did he? He's so manipulative.'

Mike thought about it and for the first time tried to look at it from Enzo's point of view. Yes, it would be a shock for his putative world champion to quit with only three races left. After all, he was a leading car manufacturer. Perhaps if Enzo had acted differently, had invited Louise to Maranello in order to pay her compensation for the loss of Pete and had not gone through the awful process of emotional blackmail he then might, just might have been persuaded to drive for one last time as suggested by Duncan and Stuart.

'Bloody hell!' he suddenly exclaimed.

Louise stared at him.

'Louise, do you remember he promised you a surprise if you went to see him? Yeah, some surprise!'

Oddly enough, although Mike was determined not to let Enzo think that he had won a victory and would announce his retirement as soon as he reached home he had no idea that, within a few days, the malevolent fates had other plans for him. His decision to drive or not would depend not on the machinations of Enzo Ferrari but on the innocence and sincerity of a 17-year-old boy. The game at that point, Mike would come to realise, could only be played one way.

\* \* \* \* \*

He could not remember much of the flight back to England as he suffered a black out en route. It only lasted for half a minute or so during which a frightened Louise had managed to get an air steward to revive him using smelling salts. Once recovered he said he felt fine. 'Just one of those things,' he said and promptly fell asleep. When he awoke the aircraft was crossing the English coast and heading for Heathrow.

Louise made him promise to see the doctor on his return home.

However, Mike did not see his doctor, nor was he able to announce his retirement as quickly as he had planned simply because Enzo had made sure that the news of his intent to carry on racing was already being published before he could give his story. Ironically, the news failed to create much of a splash because most readers of the sports pages were not even aware that he was ill and presumed that with only three races left in which to win the greatest prize of his life, something sought after by every British racing driver since world championship motor racing began, he would simply press on. Another ironical twist was that Basil Cardew, reflecting the Enzo story, caught the mood of the nation under the caption 'DO IT FOR PETE'.

The other reason that Mike had for holding back his rebuttal was that, on arriving home, he suddenly remembered that Pete's Memorial Service was fixed for the following Sunday 17 August and most of the notables of the Grand Prix racing world would be there. It would be a safe bet to assume that a number of them would want to buttonhole him if they had heard of his retirement. The thought of having to prevaricate or lie would be too much for him on such an emotional occasion, he decided. It was best to lie low until the coast was clear. Having made that decision he regarded the prospect of the Memorial Service in something not far short of unmitigated gloom.

\* \* \* \* \*

.

On Sunday 17 August the honouring of Peter Collins took place where his funeral service had been held, at Stone Church. Once again it was Canon Rees Jones who conducted the proceedings. Mike and Louise were joined by Stuart, Duncan and Harry. All three kept an eye open for any sign of Carlotta but, once again, she did not put in an appearance and the service passed off peacefully.

It was Philip Rutter, the headmaster of Alcester Grammar School, the main eulogist, who made a deep impression on Mike. Philip had made Pete a governor of the school in 1956 (his eulogy was also recorded in a letter to *The Times* newspaper).

He began by referring to the popular conception of motor racing drivers as mere 'playboys', saying that sometimes, 'Peter had to play up to that image as the press demanded it,' whereas his true nature was never revealed to the public, the more the pity.

He went on:

'Beneath that playboy exterior was a young man of great maturity and unswerving loyalty. I, personally, respected his judgment and advice. On one occasion his wise counsel saved me from a serious error in school policy. His tragic and untimely death has removed not only a racing driver of world renown but also a humble and unassuming young man endowed with wisdom and vision out of all proportion to his physical age.'

Since his visit to Maranello, Mike's conscience over Pete's death had given way to anger at the way he had been manipulated. Now, the sight of Pete's coffin had rudely kick-started his remorse and was back in full flow when Philip spoke of Pete's 'unswerving loyalty'.

In the last fortnight Mike had tried to deal with his guilt over Le Mans and Luigi by writing down notes in his defence, trying to put them all in the context of Pete's death. The Le Mans disaster, he finally decided, could have happened to anybody. It did not alter the fact that he had triggered off the carnage, albeit unwittingly. But if he had not seen the horrific consequences of his act he might have escaped the torment that had followed in its wake. There was mitigation too, in the circumstances preceding Luigi's death. Had he known the full extent of Luigi's innocent involvement with the mafia, he would probably have agreed with Pete, to save him. But Luigi had made his plea far too late.

Pete's death, on the other hand, was a personal tragedy. It affected him because he knew that his best friend had sacrificed his life choosing to help him win the world championship and in so doing had deliberately chosen to throw away his own chances of being crowned with laurels – and that after virtually handing over the same prize to Fangio in a previous season. There was plenty of guilt arising from that. Writing an objective appreciation of his conscience led, in the end, to despair.

As he attempted to join in the singing of the hymn, *Onward Christian Soldiers*, he painfully dwelt, as he had countless times since his collapse in the Bonn Clinic, upon the awful choice that he had to make and which would be irrevocable once he had made it. And it had to be soon. Did Pete demand that he drive again?

He felt a stab of unease at his surroundings. And the atmosphere in church was oppressive. It was then that he realised that Duncan and Stuart sitting next to him were trying to draw his attention to the Order of Service that he held in his hand as well as gesturing towards the pulpit. He realised then that the singing had ended, that he had been introduced and it was his moment to deliver his eulogy. There was no escape this time, no time to step aside and drag out his paper bag. He stood up, stepped into the aisle and walked towards the pulpit and climbed the steps.

Inside the pulpit he looked at the congregation staring back at him. He blinked and with a finger tip brushed a bead of sweat from over his eye. And then, as suddenly as they came, the first signs of a panic attack began to ebb away and the faces watching him became solid and still. He looked at the sheet of paper in his hand and it was no longer trembling. Pausing, to ensure that his breathing had stabilised, he heard his spoken words conveyed in a voice that was steady. He was fortunate in that his fear of a panic attack had shut out his grief and therefore, so long as he concentrated on his typewritten words, he would not break down with emotion.

It was a good speech. He was even able to deliver his joke about Pete's passion for puzzles and spoke with a touch of irony that drew some chuckles from the congregation. But the most pleasing to him was Louise's warm smile of gratitude as he rejoined her in the pews.

As they left the church, thanking the Canon, she turned to Mike and put her hand on his arm. 'That was really great Mike, thanks,' she said.

Afterwards Duncan, Stuart and Harry walked with them to look at the pile of flowers placed on and around Pete's grave. Duncan stared at him and said quietly, 'You okay?'

'Yeah.' Mike shook his head. 'I nearly went though.'

'I could see. What happened?'

'I dunno.'

They watched Louise bend down to peer at the messages written on labels attached to the flowers. He crouched down alongside her and together they commented quietly on the well-known names, not just from the world of motor racing but also from people who had shared the privilege of having known Pete. One message was from a Terry Buckland who wrote. 'I feel really bad for not being able to pay you back. What you did for me was fabulous.'

'That's mine.'

The voice was male and when Mike glanced up he saw a young man at his side, fair haired and broad faced like himself.

'I wrote that.'

Mike stood up to enquire. Terry Buckland told him that he had been a sixth former at Alcester School and at one Speech Day he had talked with Pete, then in his role as a governor, about his ambition to become a commercial pilot.

Terry's parents had little money and so when his attempt to gain free training on the BOAC pilot training course at Hamble had failed, he had turned to Pete for advice. He was amazed when Pete offered to pay for private flying lessons at a local airfield.

There, having gained his Private Pilot's Licence, it led to him being finally accepted by BOAC for their own training course and the result three years later was that Terry was now a First Officer flying one of the new Comets powered for the first time by jet engines, on their passenger service across the Atlantic. As a way of thanking Pete he had decided that he would 'somehow wangle' Pete and Louise a free return trip from Heathrow to New York. The opportunity came just after Pete's death. He deeply regretted not doing something earlier as a way of paying back his debt. He also spoke of his disappointment that he had not been called upon to speak in church so as to thank Pete posthumously, for his great act of generosity. Now it was over and his sense of guilt continued to trouble him.

Mike talked to him for several minutes as he also held a Private Pilot's Licence, before wishing him well. He then took Louise to join the rest of the congregation grouped between the church porch and the gates. A long time was spent in Louise thanking individuals for attending the service.

Later, when Mike escorted Louise to his car he turned to find the churchyard deserted. Suddenly he said, 'I'll only be a second' and went back into the churchyard to stand before Pete's grave. The parallel between Terry's guilt and his own had a moral equivalence that he could not evade. Looking down at the grave he said simply, 'Thanks mate. We'll win the championship.'

He went back to join Louise in the car and told her of his decision to carry on racing.

Louise saw from his businesslike manner of starting the car that his mind was made up.

'Okay,' she said calmly. 'I'll try to be there for you.'

She gave a little sob, but recovered quickly. 'Okay,' she said briskly. 'I might not be able to make Portugal but I might the Italian. Enzo will show me off no doubt.'

She stared through the windscreen at Duncan's car drawing away with Harry as passenger.

Since she was flying to America early the next morning Mike had arranged with Duncan to meet Stuart and Harry at The Barley Mow that evening. There, he told them of his decision, but made no mention of what had prompted it.

Stuart wanted to know if he had committed himself to the next race in Portugal or was he determined to finish the season? Mike replied that if he was 'buggered' after Portugal then he would quit. But, should he prove fit, then he would consider competing in the Italian Grand Prix. His commitment to Pete was his aim, to win the world championship, but it all depended on how he felt after each race. As Stuart had originally suggested it would be a matter of playing it by ear.

'And your bloody statistics,' he added.

Stuart laughed.

Alone with Duncan on the route home Mike was quiet for a moment and then said, 'If I get the chop anytime I don't want my mother to have to identify me. Would you do it?'

Duncan glanced at him. 'Yeah,' he said. 'But it won't happen.'

'Thanks.' Mike began to grin. 'You know something? When we started this game we did it for fun. What's happened to it?'

They laughed like it was old times.

When they reached the house they found Winifred, as so often in the afternoon, in the garden tending her plants. She had not wanted to attend the service as she feared it would have been too much for her.

Mike decided that, with Duncan as moral support, now was the time to tell her of his decision. He would say that he would only do the Portuguese, that was all. He said his piece, but instead of looking shocked Winifred remained looking at him, wearily.

Duncan, spotting his chance, stepped in quickly. 'Winn,' he said. 'Lightning's struck twice. It can't happen a third time, not with just one race. He'll be safe. I'll look after him, don't worry.'

# **Chapter** Thirteen

Mike was absolutely shattered by the death of his mon ami mate, according to Bill Morgan who continued to run Mike's TT Garage with some help from Winifred. Mike regarded Bill as family ever since his father, Leslie, had died. Bill had then undertaken tasks for the family well beyond the call of duty. Not only was he a hard working, loyal and devoted employee, but someone Mike had come to trust with his deepest of secrets. In this way he became as important to Mike as Duncan and Stuart, especially in the aftermath of the three tragedies. Whereas Mike could never completely let go of his emotions in the presence of his two friends he found it easy to let tears flow in Bill's presence. It was a useful release.

When Bill heard that Mike was 'giving it another go' in Portugal he told him that he was bonkers to even think about it. But when Mike shed a tear and said that he 'had to do it for Pete', Bill made him a mug of tea and told him not to be so bloody sentimental. Pete was dead and would never know what Mike was to achieve or fail to achieve. 'Why do it to yourself Mike? Pete would not want that, not see you injure yourself?' He said that Mike was actually being selfish and when Mike looked hurt, he made the point about Winifred.

'She's had to put up with a lot Mike. You should think about her more.'

Bill then picked up a copy of the *Daily Express* which ran the story of Stirling Moss's reaction to Pete's death and asked him to read it. Stirling was quoted as saying that motor racing was a highly dangerous sport that was bound to have death or injury as an occasional penalty for the privilege of being allowed to belt round race tracks at maximum speed in competition. Stirling also said that nobody should ever be called upon to take the blame for such happenings because – as Denis Jenkinson had said – the whole point of motor racing was the danger. If there was no risk would it not be boring? Stirling went on to say that Pete had made a mistake at a corner that was normally 'no big deal' (meaning easy to get round) and that was why it was so shocking.

Mike read the piece and came straight back with the question, 'If it was no big deal why did he crash? He crashed because of me. That's why I've got to go on Bill. I can't help it.'

At that moment a shaft of sunlight streamed through the window and caught his hair. In that instant Bill saw the popular image of 'The Golden Boy' and his feeling changed from one of irritation to that of sympathy, so much so that he winced, shook his head in apology and then gave Mike a big hug.

Louise, tying up the loose ends at her home in Worcestershire, was relieved when her father, Andrew, managed to get further leave from the United Nations to fly over again to lend a hand for a few days. She confessed to him that she was suffering so much from fears for Mike's safety as well as her bereavement that she had lost all sense of reality. She asked his advice. She had booked a meeting with Peter Ustinov in New York for Friday 22 August. Should she cancel it and go to Portugal to support Mike in the Grand Prix? Andrew told her to relax and think about herself. She had more than enough stress than to risk adding to it.

Louise admitted that there was, indeed, enough on her plate, not least the business of wrapping up a life in England that was proving far more complicated and time consuming than she had expected. With a heavy heart she telephoned Mike to give him the news that she would not be there for him in Portugal, but promised to be there for the race in Italy. She made him promise to cable her as soon as the race was over to say that he was alive and without injury.

He gave her that promise.

However, instead of easing her mind, she began to fret ahead of the Portuguese race. When her father managed to tie her down as to the reason she said, 'It's the old story. While I was at the races with Pete it was nowhere near as bad as being away. Mike's racing in Portugal and I won't be there and I'm so sick about it. Not knowing what's happening is going to be terrible.'

\* \* \* \* \*

The Portuguese Grand Prix was set for Sunday 24 August. This was to be the eighth of the 10 championship races and, as usual, points would be awarded to the first six drivers, the winner gaining eight and the runner up seven. There were now just six points separating the big, blond and heroic looking

Hawthorn and the smaller, straight talking and dynamic Moss. Their battle for top dog had sparked off speculation everywhere, opinions being voiced in British pubs and clubs throughout the land.

Oporto was to be the venue for the race, the first Grand Prix to be staged there.

As in Monaco it would take place along its streets. For most of the drivers it would present them with 4.6 miles of unfamiliar straights and corners that had been designed for road cars, not racing cars. Of all the drivers who would surmount this problem by dint of determination and concentration, it was Stirling who was the bookie's favourite to win since it was a pound to a penny bet that he would be the first to memorise the circuit. He had the knack of being able to create a pattern in his visual memory, an overall 'view' of the circuit that gave him the confidence necessary to perform at the highest level.

As the teams assembled ahead of practice the atmosphere in the pits and paddock was one of gloom. It was less than three weeks since Pete had died. Denis Jenkinson wrote that 'the relatively slow practice times in the first session, were almost a mark of respect'. He was being overly sentimental as the drivers used the session not so much as to record a time but to get used to each braking zone and the lay out of the corner ahead and so were bound to record slower lap times than usual.

By the end of the practice sessions the bookie's favourite, Stirling, had capitalised on his extra days of practice by grabbing the sought after pole position on the grid. It was regarded that it had given him a considerable advantage, since overtaking on street circuits was usually more difficult than on purpose built tracks. With this achievement Stirling recovered from his depression that had followed the British Grand Prix. He was re-energised and keen to make amends. Because his Vanwall was potentially faster in cornering than a Ferrari Dino – and so long as it stood up to the pressure – he felt that he should win the race.

Mike's fastest lap put him next to Stirling on the front row, thus intensifying expectations of a battle royal the following day. The overnight speculation among the fans had now risen to fever pitch and the *Daily Express* seized the opportunity to present Mike and Stirling as patriots abroad fighting for their country, a notable turn about from the days when the newspaper, along with the *Daily Mirror*, had criticised Mike for not serving his two years of conscription in the armed forces.

However, Mike's good performance on the track did not reflect his mental state which was down. Knowing that Stirling was favourite to win the race cast a pall over his own efforts. But he had to go on. He was committed to winning the world championship. It was a case of do or die – literally.

Stuart and Harry met with Duncan in a small café for privacy and over black coffee talked about Mike's chances. It was agreed that he needed Stirling to finish the race out of the points if Mike was not to be tasked with the final two races, the 'gut wrenching' Italian and the 'hot as hell' in Morocco. As things stood it was an odds on bet that Stirling would win. Stuart reminded them that his forecast, based on statistics, supported the general opinion. Again, it would be a case of doing what they could on the track to help Mike without prejudicing their own chances and without falling foul of the rules. As always, Stuart added, he would be ready with a spare body belt if needed. Again he was forced to mention that, as Stirling's teammate, anything he did for Mike would not be meant to jeopardise his chances.

Mike, on the eve of the race, retired early to his room. For half an hour he sat on the bed considering his situation. So far, despite a new pain flashing on and off in the small of his back, he had managed to keep up a show of good humour in the presence of members of the Scuderia and his fellow racing drivers, only dropping it in the presence of Duncan and Stuart who knew full well the stress he was undergoing.

He could not help but think about Stirling, envying him his good health and dynamism. There could be no greater contrast between the two combatants. Mike was both physically and mentally disadvantaged for the ordeal that street racing would put him through. Not only that, but his grievous sense of loss at Pete's absence had intensified now he was back at a race track. Driving for Ferrari had been a privilege in the early years, but after Pete had stepped into his life it had become nothing but a joy. Now, the forthcoming race promised nothing other than being a painful chore.

It was 10pm. As Mike got undressed he told himself that he had to maintain a professional frame of mind, the kind he had aimed at ahead of Silverstone. In order to drive a racing car at ten tenths performance in a race lasting over two hours, he needed plenty of rest beforehand. For that formidable task he enlisted the aid of a sleeping pill and pain killer, hoping to wake with the alarm clock at 8am the next morning.

In this he was successful. He woke up in a more positive frame of mind than that of the previous night. In the hotel he ate breakfast in the company of Tavoni and Taffy, telling them that he believed he could win.

It was 11am when he arrived in the paddock to find Carlotta, still dressed in black, wandering about in earnest conversation with Raymond Mays. She caught Mike's gaze, but showed no reaction and continued with her discussion on the move.

Mike watched her, his lips tight. Was she trying to lull him into a sense of false security? Would she be back on the pit counter ready to give him, yet again, the evil eye? He was distracted by Harry Schell wanting a quiet word. He said that he intended to pull over for Mike if the situation arose.

'Harry mate.' Mike lightly tapped him in the stomach. 'You're a star.'

Mike went into the motor home and found Tavoni on his own checking through some documentation.

'Tav. Is Carlotta going to be in the pits?'

Tavoni put a hand to his spectacles and adjusted them on his nose. 'She can go where she wants Mike.' He shrugged his shoulders as a gesture of helplessness. 'She reports to Enzo, not to me.'

Mike nodded grimly. He decided to let it rest. But if she got up to her wiles at the start of this race…

Once dressed in his racing outfit he went into the pits. And stopped dead. He looked around. He was breathing rapidly, his hands and face starting to sweat. 'Who did that? WHO-DID-THAT?' he shouted, pointing a finger.

Work ceased, not only in the Ferrari garage but also in garages on either side. Mechanics emerged from them to stare at Mike, his face pale with shock.

It was then that Tavoni strode into the pits to join the frozen tableau. Mike's outburst had also drawn the attention of Maurice Trintignant and Roy Salvadori in the adjacent Cooper-Climax garage. His shout had also raised the Lotus-Climax driver, Graham Hill, who was situated in the pits on the other side. Even Maria Teresa de Filippis, the Maserati driver and only female competitor in an otherwise masculine world, stood gazing at him from two garages away.

Mike continued to look at his car in fear and disbelief. In practice it had carried the number 1. It was customary for a car to retain its number through practice and into the race. But it no longer bore the same number. Now it was 22. And it was the whole number, not the number 2 on both sides of the car's front as Pete's car had been labelled in Germany, but 22 repeated on the front and rear of the bodywork.

Mike spun around looking for Carlotta but she was nowhere to be seen.

'Tav? Who changed my number! Is this a joke?!'

Tavoni took a step towards him with his arm half stretched out, calmly beckoning Mike to join him in the paddock. But, once there and before he could speak, he was subjected to Mike's rapidly told story of Carlotta at Silverstone, her association with Elvira Massingham and of how Pete's life might have been saved had his number been changed and of how Luigi had also died in a car bearing the number 2. Mike finished out of breath. Tavoni had listened anxiously but patiently. He was a well-educated man and knew that soldiers, sailors and latterly airmen of all nationalities – in fact anyone engaged in competition – were prone to superstition. Bomber pilots in World War Two often carried mascots or indulged in rituals to drive away the malevolent fates. Fighter pilots carried teddy bears or good luck charms. For Mike, as for them, it was a serious matter.

Having heard the story, instead of trying to persuade Mike to drop his demand that Carlotta be expelled immediately and Enzo informed that he had enlisted a saboteur in his team, Tavoni took the quick and necessary step to put Mike's mind into a state capable of driving a racing car for over two hours in high speed competition. He merely went back into the pits and asked Taffy Von Trips if he would be agreeable to swapping numbers with Mike. Without him realising it, he had targeted the ideal driver. Taffy was already disposed towards Mike and had no fear of numbers whatsoever.

The swap was made official after the Race Office was informed. It was ratified that Taffy's number 24 be exchanged with Mike's 22 and was recorded as a late change due to 'unforeseen circumstances'.

Mike was still unhappy that he still carried the number 2 but said 'it was a bloody sight better than 22'. Tavoni now told him to forget it and concentrate on the business of winning the race. Mike said he was happy to do that.

With 20 minutes left before he was needed, Mike returned to the motor home for a rest, but not before patting Tavoni on the arm as a gesture of apology and after giving Taffy a pat on the shoulder with a few mumbled words of apology. He knew that his outburst would be the talk of the paddock after the race. It would get into the papers by virtue of mechanics being poorly paid for their long hours, there being always one who would take the opportunity to make a bit on the side should a juicy titbit of a story come to light.

Mike returned after 15 minutes and sought out Stuart and Stirling in the Vanwall pits. He shook hands with them both.

'Have a good one, you two,' he said with a grin. 'I'll see you in my mirror.'

'The only thing you'll see in your mirror is dust,' said Stirling and gave him the two fingers.

Mike hesitated, was about to say 'Piss off' but stopped himself. 'Stirling', he said. 'Let's go out together, give 'em a thrill eh?'

'Yeah, why not,' said Stirling. 'Why not.'

The two contenders seeking the enviable title of the first British world drivers' champion walked out of the pits shoulder to shoulder. As they received a standing ovation from the crowd they shook hands for the pack of photographers before getting into their respective cars. A drizzle had started to fall and to protect their vision for as long as possible a mechanic stood over each driver holding umbrellas.

After the warm-up lap Mike sat next to Stirling on the front row of the grid, the engines all about revving and falling, the level of noise building as the flag was raised. He suddenly remembered Carlotta, was about to jerk his head round to look, but stopped himself at the last second.

The flag fell. It was Stirling who launched himself into the lead and was first to the corner, with Mike on his heels. Into the second lap Mike drew close, catching up with him on the back straight, then outbraking him into the corner. Mike led Stirling for the next six laps. Then, with the drizzle ceasing to fall and the roads drying out, Mike hoped for better cornering but – to his frustration and dismay – found that his brakes were beginning to fade. Stirling, as soon as he divined what was wrong, out braked him into the final corner of the lap, thundering into the home straight to the cheers of his fans.

At the half distance mark Stirling led Mike by a massive margin of 55 seconds. Forced into the pits by his failing brakes, Mike returned to the track and found to his horror that his brakes were, yet again, fading. Braking into a corner his car spun almost to a standstill, losing time. He knew that both Stirling and Stuart were now almost certain to finish the race one lap ahead of him. But Stirling, considering his feelings, spared him the humiliation of being lapped by slowing down to follow him over the finish line. The race was over, yet Mike, in order to collect points for third place, had to complete one more lap. Stirling, on what was his victory lap, was content to remain behind Mike, acknowledging the crowd as he went. Suddenly Mike's brakes completely failed on the approach to a corner and he shot into the 'escape road' stalling the engine. Stirling slowed down alongside and open mouthed watched him climb out and attempt to push the car. Stirling knew what he was trying to do – get the car free wheeling with the intention of jumping back inside to ram the engine into gear by which means he would restart the engine. But such was Mike's pain and exhaustion that he failed to realise that the track ahead was on an incline.

Stirling, not believing his eyes, watched Mike until, drawing even closer, he bawled out, 'Mike you clot! You won't start it going uphill!'

Mike, pale faced and slack jawed, turned his head to stare at him, his eyes glazed.

'Push it downhill!' Stirling threw an arm out at the direction from which they had come. 'Back! Turn it round, for God's sake!'

The shouted command penetrated Mike's brain. Drenched in sweat he managed to turn round the car and on the downhill managed to jump start the engine. Back at the entrance to the escape road he turned round again to continue towards the finish. He crossed the line and drove into the pits, to slump over the wheel. Thinking that the championship was now beyond him it was some time before he pulled the cotton wool out of his ears to hear Tavoni telling him that he had not been placed third after all, but second. Stuart had mistaken his own number of completed laps. He was not classified as 'finished' and so had been relegated to third place.

Minutes later, during the ceremony, Mike raised Stirling's arm as a token of his gratitude. Then he embraced Stuart and gave his mandatory big grin for the photographers before heading quickly for the motor home. He was still sitting there 20 minutes later, after having taken a pain killer and downing a litre of water. Duncan watched him in concern.

'What points have I got?' Mike let out a sigh.

'You've got 36 now. Stirling's got 32.'

Mike's response was for his head to lower again. 'You know what that means? I can't quit. I've got to do at least one more.'

Duncan was silent, thinking about Winifred, the promise they had made to her.

Mike read his mind. 'I'll tell Mum. I'll fix it with her.'

'You don't have to do it Mike. Stirling's due for at least another breakdown. You can still retire and end up champion.' Duncan was still thinking about Winifred. 'Don't forget the next one's Monza.'

The mention of 'Monza' summoned up in Mike recollection of the pain and misery he had endured during the Monza 500 race earlier that season, fought out on the high banked sweeping curves as well as the gradients that had battered his insides so badly.

However, talk of the remaining races suddenly became academic as the disturbing news came that Mike had been reported to the race stewards by a marshal for having pushed his car against the direction of the race. He was in danger of losing all of his seven points, putting Stirling into the championship lead.

Mike and Tavoni, followed by Duncan, walked to the stewards' office. There, Tavoni spoke up for Mike at the enquiry, making an impassioned appeal on his behalf. At the end of answering questions they were both asked to leave the room.

Mike was pessimistic. 'Tav, you did a great job, but I think it's over'.

As they stepped out into the sunlight, Tavoni opening his cigarette case, Stirling unexpectedly appeared, looking neat and spruce as ever. With a pat on Mike's arm he entered the office, leaving Mike exchanging glances with Tavoni and Duncan.

Was Stirling going to give evidence against him?

Stirling stood before the stewards and said that he did not want to win the championship by another's default and insisted that Mike had restarted his car on the escape road and had only turned round before its exit. That could not be described as 'driving in the opposite direction of the race', could it?

Stirling left the room to join Mike and Tavoni outside. Shortly afterwards Mike was recalled to be informed that his second place still stood and he was exonerated of all blame. When he came outside to ask Stirling what he had told the committee he found that he had vanished.

Later, after two hours of pill induced sleep, Mike hunted down Stirling to insist on buying him a drink in the hotel bar, telling him he should have won the drivers' Victoria Cross. Then added, 'You've completely done me, you know that. If you blow up in Morocco I'll have to push you as well as the bloody car.'

Stirling grinned and said, 'Mike, it's no big deal. It might have cost me the championship, but so what? I didn't want to win like that. Dead simple.'

Mike wanted to embrace Stirling but could not. When he returned to Duncan and Stuart he said he was amazed by Stirling's sacrificial act. He did not say that he had been added to his list of creditors. Instead he put it as a joke. 'How can I stop now? I can't retire because Stirling will think I did it to repay him, to help him win the championship.'

Duncan laughed. That was more of the old Mike.

Stuart added, 'Knowing Stirling he'd rather give it away.'

Oddly, as the evening progressed, Carlotta was nowhere to be seen. Apparently she had not been present in the pits during the race. Mike, on being told this, expressed his relief. Maybe now, she was finished in her evil work.

\* \* \* \* \*

The Autodromo Nazionale was situated north of Milan near the town of Monza. It was Italy's shrine to the god of speed and its packed stands during the Italian Grand Prix always welcomed home its icon, the Ferrari racing car.

However, on 7 September 1958 this regular assumption took a knock as fans stayed away in their thousands, despite the likelihood of the Scuderia de Ferrari winning the world championship in terms of it becoming the top scoring constructor. They might worship the *machina* but their beloved driver, Luigi Musso, was dead. The ranks of the tifosi mourned his loss and labelled Enzo Ferrari a coward and a traitor for not replacing Luigi with another Italian. The fill-in driver was Phil Hill, the American.

The fans also lambasted Enzo for having promised to attend the race, having told his work force and the public at large. Some, having read an editorial in *Il Osseratore Romano*, believed it when its leader condemned Enzo as acting like the 'god Saturn, consuming his own sons'.

Adding to their cup of bitterness was the fact that the entire four car front row was given over to solely British drivers, with Stirling Moss on pole position, alongside him Tony Brooks and next to him, Mike and Stuart. And with two British built Vanwalls dominating the single Ferrari at the head of the pack the disaffection of the fans was complete.

Basil Cardew had already written the opening lines of his copy for the *Daily Express*: 'The titanic struggle between Britain's greatest drivers came to a head today in the spiritual capital of world motor racing, Monza.'

He then drove the patriotic knife deeper by referring to Dunlop helping Ferrari by helping them fit disc brakes to Mike's car. Why could they not aid the other British hopeful, Stirling Moss, who was driving a British car?

The day before final practice Louise sent Mike a cable from New York to say that at the last minute she had managed to free herself from rehearsals in order to be at Monza – and could he book a room for her? In arranging the trip she had put herself to great inconvenience in missing her father's birthday. She held back from telling Mike that, while the Portuguese Grand Prix was being staged, she had not been able to eat breakfast such was her nervousness and had only started to breathe properly when she learnt that he had survived.

After her arrival and a few hours' rest she joined Mike to chat over a drink in the bar. She voiced her annoyance that Enzo had failed to keep his promise of being there and that she would never believe another word the man said. She thought that the Italian fans were justified in castigating him for not signing at least one Italian driver for the race.

'Can you imagine the Boston Red Sox not fielding an American in the team?'

She found Mike smiling at her. 'What...?'

He placed a hand on her arm. 'I wish I'd got a big sister like you.'

She laughed modestly. And then Mike stiffened at the sight of the woman in black making her appearance with Tavoni.

Louise saw his face tauten. 'What is it?' she said in a whisper.

'It's Carlotta. I thought she'd gone. This is ridiculous.'

Mike was unlucky not to know that Carlotta's desire for revenge had ended with Pete's death and that she was attending races now purely as Enzo's spy. The truth was that she was now one of Enzo's mistresses and had been 'loaned' a Ferrari road car. It would not be long before she owned one. Her mourning now seemed to have metamorphosed into one of comfortable sadness.

On the morning of the race Mike encountered Stirling at breakfast.

'How's it going?' he said cheerfully.

'I'm terrified,' said Stirling, equally cheerful, then became serious. 'Mike, if my engine conks out today and you win, you're world champion. But if you see me down an escape road don't stop. You promise?'

'Why are you such a goody goody?' Mike said and broke out into a big grin.

'It's called softening up the opposition Mike,' said Stirling, returning the grin.

Mike later confessed to Louise that Stirling was not just a great driver but an incredible man. 'He's dead honest. Everything he sees is in black and white. It's right or it's wrong. He never bullshits, never worries about his conscience because he doesn't need to.'

In the heat of the early afternoon a large pack of cameramen assembled at the trackside to photograph Stirling and Mike shaking hands. The two of them then shook hands with Stuart and Tony Brooks before climbing into their cars on the front row.

As Mike settled down in the cockpit he took his last swig of water and handed the bottle back to his mechanic. As he did so he caught Stuart looking at him from a few metres away giving him the thumbs up. Mike returned the gesture.

As the countdown began Mike became concerned that the intermittent pain felt just above the curve in the small of his back, was intensifying. He carried three of the strong painkillers in his jacket pocket. In this regard he had only two options.

He could drive in a manner that would flood his system with adrenalin – that meant gambling his life on 'the ragged edge' – as had Luigi – or he could take a painkiller that could give rise to slower reactions as well as a dullness of mind. He decided on the former. Taking a pill could lead to disaster, should his reactions be badly affected.

Having made the decision he knew that he had to be brave as well as lucky on this, the fastest track in the world. The g-forces would be huge. But he had to go out to win, as only maximum points would provide him with enough margin on which to retire and await the result of Stirling's last race of the season in Morocco. The world championship could be won at Monza, he decided.

The pain, he realised, was a fraction less intense with the adrenalin kick before the race start. He put down his vizor. He was ready.

Louise, meanwhile, was sitting down in the race commentary tower at the behest of one of the circuit owners who happened to have seen her perform on Broadway. At first she had graciously declined but then had thought about it, coming to the conclusion that seeing all of the race from her high point would be less agonising than sitting in the pits forced to wait for Mike to reappear each lap. She found herself accepting the offer.

Mike watched the starter raise his flag and went into launch mode, but a sudden stab of pain, totally unexpected, caused him to tauten the muscles in his stomach and back. He lost concentration as the flag fell.

'Fuck!'

He botched his launch, his wheels spinning and clutch burning. In those opening seconds he had negated all the good work that had been done in fitting the Dino with disc brakes. Moreover, having damaged his clutch, he would be fortunate if it lasted the race. He finally got away in a cloud of scorched rubber. He knew that his chances of winning the race were remote, so far ahead were the front runners.

The stage was now set for one of the most remarkable recoveries in motor racing and would show Mike Hawthorn as a truly great racing driver, despite his grave handicaps.

Louise, watching from the tower, saw Mike's car enter the Curva Grande with the leaders already halfway down the straight ahead. She saw Phil Hill, the fourth Ferrari driver, disappear into the Curva di Lesmo, one of the steeply banked sections of the track. Then, in a flash, two following cars collided as they approached the first corner. In a blur of blood red and British racing green they flew over the fencing and into the trees beyond.

Louise clapped a hand to her mouth in horror. It could not be Mike – his start was delayed. But who were they?

Mike saw the same accident from behind, knowing that one was a Ferrari, denoted by its distinguishable blood red colour, but the other had been difficult to fix.

Was the Ferrari driven by Taffy Von Trips? Or Olivier Gendebien, the third driver in the Ferrari team?

As he raced past the accident scene Mike shut his mind to further conjecture as there was no sign of an injured driver nor, remarkably, was there any wreckage on the track. He had no means of identifying which drivers were involved. In any event trying to attempt rational thought was impossible when all of his being was devoted to racing and trying to shut out pain that was only just tolerated by the adrenalin 'high'.

In sweated concentration he focused on dealing with the Curva di Lesmo. Even the wearing of two body belts did not save him from having to hold back his breathing and simultaneously tense his abdominal and neck muscles to avoid the risk of passing out through a g-force of four and a half times his body weight. His punishment was made the greater by the curved high banking creating vertical, as well as lateral, g-forces.

At the end of the first lap he had Stuart in his sights. Slowly, he made up the ground between them, at which the crowd, thrilled by the sight of a Ferrari attacking the British Vanwall, began to cheer him on. On this day Mike had no time for the customary wave or grin as he overtook, though Stuart waved an arm in encouragement.

Mike found himself fighting a battle on two fronts, one dealing with the intensifying pain, the other fighting his way through the field. Now he could see the green tail of the second Vanwall driven by Stirling. The crowd, sensing that the Ferrari was about to overtake the British car, bellowed out in encouragement. As he entered the home straight the fans in the seated areas rose to their feet as he overtook Stirling and then set about pulling back his next target, Phil Hill.

By now Louise had learnt that the drivers who had crashed were Taffy Von Trips and Harry Schell. Taffy, in a repeat image of Pete at the Nürburgring, had been thrown out of his car, but had the good fortune to land between trees, his body thumping into the soft bed of fir needles to only suffer from bruising. His car was shattered into small pieces in the crash whereas Harry's BRM had remained more or less intact. Harry's luck had been derived, not by his ejection from the car, but by having remained within it, with the car impacting not far from Harry. His injuries were cuts that only required a few stitches. It had been a miraculous escape for them both.

On hearing this, Louise had begun to follow the race once more, her finger nails digging into the palms of her hands, willing Mike on to take the lead in safety.

On the fifth lap Mike finally overhauled Phil Hill, bringing the crowd once more to its feet, not applauding the *machina* now, but its driver. Mike, the archetypal Englishman, had won their affection. His achievement, unknown to them, was the more amazing because he was making his rapid charge through the field while suffering from increasing pain.

The adrenalin flow could not match it. Even so he continued to drive impeccably, braking and entering corners at precisely the right moment and taking the exact racing line. If, by a split second, he left his braking too late he would lose the correct entry point, losing the line. If he braked too soon he would lose time. He remembered always to compensate for the tendency of his car to understeer by entering the corner with the lightest of brake pressure. It was as if his mind were detached from his body, in tune with the demands of the race. He had settled into a rhythm that prompted automatic reactions. He had no idea of the excitement he was generating around the circuit. With his ears blocked by cotton wool and with the roar of the engine he was oblivious to the crowd noise as much as he was to the commentator's excited commentary over the public address system.

But no amount of sweet timing and balanced cornering could prevent him from tiring and as a result he was gradually losing ground to the Vanwalls of

Stirling and Stuart, even the BRM of Jean Behra. As a result he dropped back into third place. But then something utterly incredible happened. The tiredness vanished. Once again he was able to summon up every ounce of energy in his body. Defying all the odds he managed, with a supreme effort, to take back the lead on lap 17.

On the next lap he had the stroke of luck that brought back into view what had seemed until minutes ago the most dimmest of targets, the world championship. For once the malevolent gods ceased their partying as the lap board held out to him by an excited Ferrari mechanic told him that Stirling had retired from the race, having suffered from another mechanical failure. 'Michael Hawthorn diventa campione del mondo se vince la gara!' The commentator's voice said it all.

It was now a straightforward task, entirely in his own hands. All he needed to do was to remain in the lead over the next 52 laps and he would take the greatest prize ever to be won by a British driver. At that moment he was, as Basil Cardew scribbled on his note pad, 'within touching distance of the trophy'.

However, the reality was that he would have to withstand one and a half hours of mental and physical torture. Even the fittest and strongest of drivers found Monza one of the most demanding race tracks in Grand Prix motor racing. He might conceivably finish the race but in what position? The odds on taking any points from the race were still heavily stacked against him, given that his energy level was bound to drop as the race went on. The strong likelihood was that he would hit the 'wall', the metaphorical barrier at which his mind and body would simply refuse to keep operating at a consistently high level of performance. How would he manage, during that eternity, to still continue hitting his braking points with metronomic regularity, follow the correct racing line for each corner as well as make the gear changes at the appropriate time?

By the end of lap 31 – and with 39 laps left – he was forced into the pits for a tyre change. While it took place he hastily drank a half bottle of water, splashing the rest down his front collar and neck. It revived him a little as he set off again to rejoin the race in third place. Still he fought back the pain and still he managed to keep to each racing line, that is until lap 37 when he lay second to Phil Hill, the race leader, who stopped for a wheel change.

Mike suddenly found himself back in the lead, but with one hour of racing left he realised that the inevitable would happen. He was not a robot. The pain was now dominant again and soaking up his energy at too fast a rate. He reached into his gabardine jacket and grabbed the loose painkillers. They were there for such an emergency and was not this an emergency? It mattered little if he failed by taking them as without them he was going to fail anyway – and was it not better to do it pain free?

Allied to his loss of confidence was despair when he realised that his clutch was losing its grip, an inevitable consequence of having partially burnt it out on the start line. However, this setback was balanced a little in terms of his ability to race by the three painkillers having a quick effect. Nevertheless, he began to lose ground while still in the lead on the 50th lap. Entering the home straight he glanced in his mirror to see the Vanwall of Tony Brooks appear for the first time, eight seconds behind. With 15 laps left the gap had narrowed to five seconds.

With 10 laps to the race finish the two cars appeared side by side in front of the main grandstand, jockeying for position, almost touching each other. Irrespective of them being British drivers the crowd in the main grandstand were on their feet cheering on Mike as well as the machine. Only minutes remained of the race.

It was Tony who was first into the corner. Mike desperately looked into his mirrors and saw Phil Hill now on his tail and closing. Mike, in anguish, saw himself finishing in third place. With another tremendous effort he led Phil into the final lap two seconds in the clear. Here he was helped by fortune favouring the brave as Phil was confused by his own pit signals, not knowing whether to remain behind Mike or overtake. But he knew that Enzo Ferrari would not appreciate the temporary driver in his team ruining the chances of the only driver who could lift the world championship trophy. And so Phil followed Mike over the finish line. The race was over.

Utterly exhausted, Mike, for the second race in a row, remained in his car on return to the pits. It was Duncan who managed to get a reaction by sponging water down his neck while telling him that he was eight points clear of Stirling in the championship table.

'What's that mean?' murmured Mike, his eyes closed and taking a drink of water from a bottle.

'It means, old son, that if Stirling wins in Morocco you only have to finish in second place to be world champion!'

Mike staggered out of the car and had to be held upright. The prize giving ceremony for Tony Brooks, the winner, had to be held up for a few minutes while Mike was taken to the Medical Centre where the doctor thought he was merely dehydrated. His secret remained.

After the ceremony Mike embraced Tony for the photographers. He went back to the motor home when Stuart and Harry, the latter showing bruises on his face from the crash, came along to see him. Harry produced a hip flask and after a 'nip or two' Mike was taken back to the hotel by Duncan where Louise insisted that he had some sleep. He was supposed to be escorting her that night to the Principe de Savoia Hotel in Milan where a dinner was to be held in honour of Juan Fangio's retirement. She felt that she would enjoy it, but only if joined by a refreshed Mike.

He slept soundly for two and a half hour hours and then, with another pain killer inside him, insisted on taking a protesting Louise to the Hotel, still anxious about him. After the reception they sat down to dinner and Mike asked her why she was so tense. Something was bothering her. What was it? At first she prevaricated and then was forced into an admission.

'I'm sorry, Mike, but that was awful seeing Taffy and Harry in that crash. I thought they were dead. I just can't face it again. I know it's the last race but...'

She stopped talking as Mike squeezed her hand. 'It's okay. I don't blame you. We're all mad as hatters. Anyway, I thought you said Peter Ustinov wanted you then.'

'He does Mike. But I could have got out of it.'

'Don't.' Mike squeezed her hand again.

Grateful, she demanded that he telephone her day or night following the race. It did not matter the circumstances. She simply needed to know that he was safe.

'Oh Mike, one thing I forgot. If you have to send me a cable it's to Louise King, not Collins. I'm going back to my stage name.'

\* \* \* \* \*

Winifred had spent an awful time escaping from the house during the staging of the Portuguese Grand Prix and then the Italian. There was a six week wait before the final race in Morocco. Hurt and martyred, having been lied to by Mike, she told him that she had given up worrying. He might as well do the last race. She said she was going to Bournemouth for a few days, for some sea air and rest and would not bother to find out the race result until she was back home. Because she made little eye contact with Mike, tending to ignore him, she failed to notice the changes in Mike's face, the extra fattening to the cheeks, for example.

On Monday 15 September Mike made a visit to Guy's Hospital, having contacted the consultant worried that his second battering of the year from the curved high banked track at Monza, might have done irreparable damage. He had reason to be worried. Apart from the pain in his back he had started to feel more tired than usual, even when just sitting around. He also felt cold, when normally he was a warm person. He had also noticed a slight swelling of his ankles.

He was relieved to find that the consultant, who had seen him on the previous occasion, had been replaced by the familiar and friendly, if sometimes grumpy, Scotsman. The usual blood and urine tests were carried out, plus one or two others that were new to procedure, including an overall examination of his body.

Yes, on being questioned he admitted that he was aware of a slight thickening of his ankles, but thought that he had been told that he was likely to suffer from such as a result of taking the kind of pills prescribed for him? The consultant thought it was more indicative of his kidney problems. He seemed more thoughtful than usual and made no reference to his chances of becoming world champion.

On Friday 19 September in the early afternoon, Mike was at his TT Garage talking with a mechanic, when the telephone rang. It was the consultant's office, asking if he could make an appointment for the following week 'to discuss the test findings'.

Mike agreed to the appointment and spent the next few days worrying about it. He told no one, not even Duncan who rang to discuss the contract they were to mutually sign, marking their partnership in a new business. Enzo had granted Mike the British concession for selling and servicing Ferrari road cars, his way of thanking him for all his achievements, whether he won the world championship or not. Mike had invited Duncan to join him in the business, his own way of thanking his best mate. Not only would they sell Ferraris but also Duncan's special love, the marque he had raced – the same one that Mike specialised in at the TT Garage – Jaguars. When their signing of the contract had taken place they would mark the occasion by inviting all their friends to a special celebration.

Mike kept the appointment at Guy's Hospital on Monday 22 September at 11am. At first the consultant talked about the tests that Mike had undergone and then referred to his recent bouts. It all added up, he said, to signs that his remaining kidney was in trouble. He paused a moment and then continued, 'There is work being done in America in transplanting kidneys and I'm sure that dialysis will improve to be available to more people, even possibly at home, but it's a long shot. It's all a matter of time. Unfortunately it's time you haven't got, I'm afraid.'

Mike's initial reaction as the doctor started talking was one of concern that, yet again, he was to be told of the silliness of battering his body with g-forces. So used to switching off when he was being lectured, he failed to concentrate and only came to realisation with the consultant's final sentence.

Mike stared at him. 'Are you saying I…I'm dying?'

'I'm afraid so, Mike.'

He paused, transfixed. 'How long?' His own voice seemed to come from far away.

'Well, it's difficult. Possibly a year – at the outside.'

He paused and waited for Mike to speak. On 1 September a circular had been sent to all doctors by the NHS on the importance of thinking carefully about the imparting of bad news. It was stressed that it was important to give the patient time to absorb what they had been told.

Mike's gaze dropped to the file that lay on the desk, his file, a bulging file.

The consultant coughed, paused and then said, 'I'm going to write to your GP and get him to take over. You'll be needing stronger painkillers for some time. Once they stop working he'll move you on to morphine. As I said, there won't be any pain at all then, so no need to be afraid.'

# **Chapter** Fourteen

During the next three days Mike thought of committing suicide and then dismissed it, thinking of his mother and the trauma it would put her through. The panic and horror filled moments were punctuated by a surge of rage at the injustice of it all, at one point lashing out at his prize winning cups, sending them crashing to the floor. It had brought Winifred in haste fearing that he had suffered another blackout, only for him to say that he had stumbled.

His decision had been to tell no one, not out of concern for their feelings but for his own. It was a piece of dim logic, thinking that if he did impart the news to anyone their reaction would be one of such horror that it would put himself into shock, that they would present him with the stark reality of the coming of death, something he was trying to deal with. He used the technique employed at Reims, writing notes to the effect that death was a mere nothing. 'You, the dead, cannot be dead since you would never know it. You, as nothing, would be as you were before you were born, nothing.'

In being nothing there would be no sadness, no misery, no pain. The more he meditated the more he drew strength from it. He was not going to tell anyone.

But in sleep there was terror. He would wake in a sweat and struggle to switch on the light, only for the reality of things around him – the bedside cabinet, the wardrobe, a chair – to produce a surge of self pity and a worry that his sobbing would awaken his mother. The small hours, when the pang of knowing was frightening and when denial was impossible, were the worst.

On the fourth day he managed to give a passing thought to the now meaningless business of motor racing and winced at a ghastly joke that passed into his mind: yes, he could win the world championship but it would be pointless.

On the same day he watched Winifred as she sat in the garden and for the first time in his life thought about her relationship with his father. He could not remember seeing them kiss each other or even pass a kind word through all the years of his life. He could not remember receiving a childhood cuddle from either of them nor, as he grew up, any comforting pat on the shoulder. For that he blamed his father, always on the go, rarely settling down inside the house, often out 'chasing women' according to Winifred and he had no reason to doubt it. But was that because she was cold and distant? Which came first, his disaffection or her frigidity? And how had it all translated into his own life and behaviour? Had his own conduct, the constant yearning for convivial company and search for praise and glory, had all of that stemmed from that icy relationship?

'Mike, you promised you'd announce your retirement after Portugal. When are you going to do it?'

Winifred's voice at breakfast jolted him out of his black reverie.

'Tomorrow mum.'

'It's always tomorrow.' She paused. 'You're very quiet. Are you alright?'

'Yes. I'm fine.'

How long ago it all seemed, the all enveloping guilt following the tragedies of Le Mans, Luigi Musso and Pete Collins. None of it mattered now. What was the point of feeling, let alone doing, anything? He was as good as dead. He wished it would come quickly.

On the fifth morning he was alone in the house with Winifred out shopping, when once more a bout of fear turned into panic that was so devastating that he picked up the telephone, intending to pour it all out to Duncan but, after a hesitation, found himself telephoning Stuart instead.

'Stuart, how you doing?' He could not hide the tension in his voice.

'Okay Mike. You alright?' Stuart's voice was bright and lively. 'How's it all going?'

'Okay...I...I want to talk about something. Can we meet?'

Stuart, sensing his desperation, decided not to question him and suggested that they met in The Duke of Cambridge Hotel in Farnham. No, of course he did not mind the drive there and back. If Mike needed help he would be there for him, of course he would. He was only too pleased that he had been called upon proving, if there still lingered any doubt, that Mike regarded him as a genuine friend. Some months earlier he had visited his local Odeon cinema and sat with his wife in the rear stalls watching the Pathe newsreel screened between the 'B' film and the main feature. There came a fanfare heralding the appearance on screen of Mike, putting on a big grin following his victory in Reims, with the commentary voice telling the world that 'The Golden Boy' was 'back on top form' and 'matching Stirling point by point in the fight to become Britain's first world drivers' champion'.

Watching the big, heroic looking man, Stuart had felt insignificant, a nobody. No one ever recognised him in the street and nobody in the cinema. No press photographer was ever eager to get his picture. It was, therefore, something of a stimulus to get Mike's call for help. Okay, he was not Mike's best friend, that role being reserved for Duncan, but having been chosen as a shoulder to weep on, he felt warm and proud in that special relationship.

The lounge bar at 12.30pm was empty when they walked in, Stuart insisting on buying the drinks and having brought them to the table sat down, feeling awkward. He watched Mike take a sip of beer, noting his pale, drawn look, despite the fattening around the cheeks.

'Has it got worse Mike?' He spoke quietly, looking and sounding sympathetic.

'Yeah. The doc said I'm on my way out.' Mike winced and let out a gasp that was midway between a laugh and a sob, as if agreeing how ridiculous it all was.

'Oh Mike. Oh bloody hell.' Stuart instinctively put out a caring hand and then suddenly withdrew it, without making contact. Bullied at school because of his size, Stuart had taken up motor racing to succeed in a 'he man' sport but still could not shake off his feeling of inferiority. All he could do by way of a reaction was to put a hand to his forehead and run it backwards, flattening his hair and holding it there, looking shocked and bewildered.

'What do you mean by "on the way out"? It can't...who said? I mean, have you been seen by the top people?'

'Yeah.' Mike told him of the family doctor's visit and of his belief that waiting for future advances in renal surgery might come too late. 'So the odds aren't great.'

'But there is a chance. Come on, there is a chance,' Stuart urged. He put both hands on the table, gesturing with them. 'Mike. It could happen. I read about a kidney transplant from somebody who'd just died. About a year ago. It was in America. You mustn't give up hope, for God's sake. Promise me you won't.'

'If I thought I stood a chance...'

'You do. Of course you do. Keep going. Things will happen so you've got to keep going.'

'Go where?' Mike gave him a thin ironic smile. He felt that Stuart was touching in his sincerity, but irritating in his eagerness to please. He made him promise not to tell anyone other than Harry, not wanting it spread beyond his friends. He said he had already told Duncan, which was a lie, but felt he needed to say it as Stuart might have thought that he favoured him more than Duncan, which both knew not to be the case.

Stuart promised to keep the secret as instructed.

'You know what? said Mike. 'Enzo wrote to me, said if I won the championship he'd let me sign my own contract for next year. Said he'd sign it without even reading it. For the first time ever, real money. I could do him for thousands. Fantastic isn't it? And bloody meaningless.' He winced.

Stuart was energetic in his response. 'Mike, for God's sake, do it, take the money, sign it! You told me how he treated you and Louise. How many years have you been with him – four?'

'Five. I can't sign it if I don't race. That's fraud.' He frowned at Stuart who looked surprised. He had always felt that Mike and his fellow hearties looked on the world as their playground, to exploit. He had never thought of them as having a code of altruism. He nodded humbly in acceptance. 'Yeah, but if you don't give up, if you carry on for a race or two you can sign it, can't you?'

Afterwards, as they left the pub to stand outside in the drizzle, Mike felt ashamed that, in not ringing Duncan, he had called upon the little man, had got him to leave his family and drive a round trip of 60 miles, not because he wanted him to help but just to bloody well listen. It was worse, because in the event he had told him nothing, except the bare facts. He had made no appeal to Stuart's intelligence and nothing had been spoken about the bigger issues of coping, of coming to terms, of finding solace. He was angry with himself. Duncan was his best mate and should have been his first port of call, but he had taken the coward's way out. He wanted to apologise to Stuart, but could not, reminiscent of the moment in Reims when he had decided against confiding in him, mainly because he felt it would be demeaning to open up his veins to someone so small and weak looking. As he said goodbye to Stuart he suddenly lowered his arms to embrace him, bear like. 'Thanks mate,' he said in a rough voice and broke quickly away before the tears showed.

\* \* \* \* \*

Mike knew that he would have to tell Duncan, albeit placing him in an impossible situation. Their relationship had always been a joining of adventurous spirits, sharing a sense of cynical humour that not only excluded sentimentality and anything religious but also any aspect of things unmanly, like death or dying. Duncan would simply not have the tools in his emotional locker to deal with it. It would cut the heart out of their relationship. He might even make excuses for them not to meet again.

But it was not to turn out like that. Stuart, on arriving home, had wasted no time in ringing Harry who, after expressing his shock, had sat down to pen a letter to Mike that he posted with the ink barely dry on the paper. It arrived by first post the next morning:

'Mike, old pal, I've just heard from Stuart. It's tough news but I want you to know that we're all there for you. I don't want to keep banging on about D-Day and what happened afterwards, but I know that dying is no great deal, not when you're dead, anyway. Up to that point you've got to live for every moment, okay? Go for the world championship. Go for it. We're all going to die and we might never get anywhere near where you are, so do what you've been trying to do all these years, win those laurels. Stuart told me that if you hold on you've got a chance of getting a kidney transplant. You would kick yourself if you didn't go for it and you got well again. Pity you're not a Buddhist. They live for the moment. You've got to do the same, old buddy. Drive that Ferrari one last time. If you don't I'll be round at your place dragging you there, okay?'

Harry's gung-ho letter gave Mike a brief stab of inspiration and in that moment recalled once again the two lines from the epitaph that were now even more appropriate:

'One crowded hour of glorious life
is worth an age without a name'

But the excitement dissipated within minutes and he returned to the grey bleakness of a day that held no promise whatsoever, asking himself the reason why he had still not announced his retirement. Was it because deep down, submerged beneath his distress, lurked his need to continue? Racing was in his blood, wasn't it? It always had been, ever since winning two Novice Cups in his first motorbike 'scrambles' at the age of 16. That memory helped make up his mind. He had a pub evening scheduled with Duncan for the Wednesday evening but could not face it and so decided to give him the bad news over the telephone when it would be easier. However, on hearing Duncan's voice, his nerve went. After a hesitation he said that he was not feeling too great and the latest hospital prognosis was 'a bit iffy' and he had been ordered not to drive at Casablanca but thought 'sod it, what have I got to lose?'

Duncan paused before speaking. In a level voice he agreed that it would be 'bloody crackers' to give up now when he was so near to the crown. Mike thought it significant that, contrary to what Stuart would have done,

Duncan had not asked what he had meant by the euphemistic phrase, 'a bit iffy'. Did he suspect that he was seriously ill? Or did he know?

As the days drew nearer to departure, Winifred had taken notice of a change in Mike's appearance. And she had seen a spot of blood inside the WC basin. She begged Mike to give up the race in Morocco. Mike assured her that his last visit to hospital had been merely a check-up. This, she refused to believe and had grounds for it, hadn't she?

Mike, tired of it all, asked Duncan to come over and for one last time employed the counselling skills that had always succeeded in the past. This he did and won the day by utilising his diplomatic skills against all her protests, showing that he was not merely the 'beer drinking hearty' lacking all sensitivity, as portrayed by some.

He wrote down on a piece of paper a note, the gist of which was his assurance that if Mike ever sat in a racing car again after Morocco it would be the end of their friendship and the cancellation of their Ferrari contract. Winifred liked Duncan, but was angry with herself afterwards for allowing herself to be manipulated. She could hardly believe his sincerity, but nevertheless kept the note.

Duncan, for the latter part of the year, had not been oblivious to Mike's condition. As the weeks and months went by it was clear to him that the fattening of his face and the pale 'peaky' look together with periodic displays of tiredness, could not be ignored. But what he really found alarming were the stories of his blackouts. Louise had told him of one that had struck him on the flight home from Germany. If Morocco had not been listed as the last race of the season and one that gave him every chance of being crowned world champion, Duncan would have sided with his mother and insisted that he quit.

Tony Vandervell had chartered a Vickers Viscount for his Vanwall team. With some seats left vacant, he invited certain guests to join them. Mike, together with Duncan, accepted readily. The atmosphere inside the aircraft was quiet and businesslike – until Mike entered, to be greeted by a few good natured whistles and boos from the Vanwall mechanics.

'Where's Stirling?' Mike said, looking round the cabin.

Stuart, sitting with Tony Brooks, told him that he was travelling on the 'Grand Prix Special' as it was more convenient for Katie, his wife.

Mike put his head back and roared, 'Oh come on!' He's scared shitless. Can't even sit with me. You blokes haven't got a cat in hell's chance.' He sat down to more jibes and laughter, but in the relative seclusion of his window seat, with Duncan sitting next to him, he could drop all his pretence. He closed his eyes and tried to rest.

Basil Cardew, sitting nearby, observed his pale face and put it down to a bout of nocturnal hell raising. He then returned to the notepad. He had scribbled some headlines ahead of the race. One was in large block capitals and was the one he preferred – though what his editor might do with it was another matter. 'SHOWDOWN IN THE SUN' he thought, summed it all up. Maybe his editor could arrange for a cartoon to accompany the story. Two gunfighters confronting each other in the wild west, possibly?

The flight to Morocco was smooth and calm, without any bumps or shakes. Somewhere over southern Spain Mike woke up to find Duncan asleep, rumbling gently.

He looked at him reflectively. Should he have told him? No. Would Stuart or Harry tell him what they knew? No, he doubted it very much. They would either assume he knew as his best mate, but in any case would not want to upset him.

* * * * *

The last race in the Grand Prix calendar for 1958 was to be held for the first time as a world championship event at the dusty Ain-Diab circuit near Casablanca. The ruling king had initiated the project by first appealing to the Grand Prix organisers, declaring that October was the 'perfect tourist month' when temperatures there averaged 22 degrees Celcius, thereby making it pleasant for Europeans as well as Americans.

Mike, on arrival at the team hotel, made straight for his room. He had not been there 10 minutes when there came a knock at the door.

It was Stuart, looking upset. Mike quickly ushered him inside and shut the door.

'Mike,' Stuart said. 'Tony and me, we've been given orders to keep you out. You know if Stirling's going to win the championship he's got to finish first and you mustn't come second. So…' He flapped his arms in frustration. 'It won't be illegal, certainly not from me, but…' He was forced to break off, nearly in tears. 'Sorry.'

Mike patted Stuart's shoulder. 'It's okay mate. Phil Hill and Olivier, they'll do the same for me against Stirling. Taffy Von Trips is not driving here so it's two against two, "even stevens", don't worry about it.'

'Okay. That's good. I just didn't want you to…'

Mike grasped his shoulder and shook it. 'Look. You chaps have done all you could. I'm okay. I'm fine. And don't go easy with me at any time. I want to win this thing properly, okay?'

'Yeah. But don't…'

'No buts! Now bugger off, stop nursing me.'

'Okay.' Stuart nodded with a sigh and a smile. 'Okay Mike.' He turned to go and then stopped. 'Oh, there is one thing.'

'What now?' Mike grinned. Stuart was incorrigible.

'It's going to be hot and humid out there. Tony rang up for a weather forecast. Make sure you drink plenty of water and have you got your two body belts?'

'Yeah, I have! Bloody hell it's like I'm in a kindergarten. Now off!' Mike opened the door. Stuart, with a grin, stepped outside into the corridor. Mike watched him go, then called after him, warningly.

'Eh!'

Stuart stopped and half turned.

'If I win I'm gonna put some weight on you. You're too thin. I'll buy you the biggest fish and chips you've ever had.'

The next morning Stuart's relayed prediction came true. Gentle winds from the sea had brought a higher temperature than the average for the time of year. Not only that but the humidity level was greater than was usual for October. Before practice began at 11am the track temperature had risen to a maximum of 55 degrees Celcius.

However, there was another threat that worried Mike more than the weather. He had been first into the Ferrari pit before breakfast and found that his car once again, bore the number 2. His first thought was, once again, 'Carlotta', though he had not seen her, either alone or with any of the Ferrari team. He went back to the dining room and there was Raymond Mays at a table, without any sign of her, or Elvira. Regardless, it was another drain on Mike's nervous system. He told Duncan about it over his cornflakes. 'Luigi and Pete both had it. Superstitious or not, I'm not having it.'

'Okay. I'll fix it.' Duncan sighed and left Mike to sort out his problem. He spent a few minutes talking with Tavoni and then joined Olivier Gendebien who was at a table with Phil Hill. He reported that Olivier had agreed to swap his number 6 for Mike's number 2.

'How many more stars do I have to give you?' said Mike.

'Just write down a list of things,' Duncan replied. 'Numbers, colours, body belts. I'm the fixer.'

They exchanged grins and then Mike tucked into a cooked breakfast of sausage and bacon. Duncan, observing, thought here was one who could not be that ill.

Mike took part in the first practice session without taking one of the strongest painkillers so far, newly prescribed by the consultant. He would have used them had he needed them. Luckily, as he stepped into his car the knifelike pain that had been dogging him, had now been replaced by a dull ache in the back. Although persistent, it was controllable. For the race he had planned to have, as in Italy, some loose tablets within easy reach. Just in case…

It was during the last practice session of the following day when, in the final minutes, he put in a flying lap that gave him pole position. Instead of coming into the pits he carried on for another tour of the circuit, to stop in front of the large crowd of British fans who had heard the news over the loudspeakers. As he received numerous pats on the back, the young man from Reims who had tried to stop him with a glass of beer, was trying to get to him once more with another foaming tankard, when two celebrating fans combined to jog his arm and spill all its contents. Mike laughed heartily and then dropped his grin as he left the scene. The sharp pain had returned.

Back in the motor home, with one of the newly prescribed painkillers inside him, he felt exhausted. The weather forecast for the race promised high temperatures and humidity. How would he cope for over two hours sitting in what amounted to a Turkish bath of a cockpit, having been worn out after practice, having spent no more than 20 minutes on the track per session? He remembered Stuart's advice about drinking lots of water before the race on the following afternoon.

Before dinner that night Harry Schell came to see him in his room. Was there anything, anything at all, that he could do for Mike before or during the race? Unlike Stuart, who was committed to helping Stirling, his teammate, Harry had no such qualms. Even if it meant deliberately blocking out a driver who threatened to overtake Mike, he was up for it. Mike told him what he had told Stuart, that he wanted to 'win the thing on his own'. It would take away his sense of achievement if he was helped unfairly.

Harry nodded. 'I know what you mean Mike. Where's the prize?'

He got up to leave and stopped at the door. 'Have you heard of Tecumseh, Mike? He was an Indian chief who fought the whites trying to steal his Indian land.'

Mike shook his head.

'Well, he became such a hero that all Americans who loved freedom honoured him. We had a warship named after him. The USS *Tecumseh*. It was used by the Union against the Confederates. Sunk in 1864. He was quite a guy. He wrote stuff, poetry and things.'

'About?' said Mike.

'Dying and living your life. Some of it is really good.'

'You're going to tell me some.'

'A few lines.' He paused:

> 'When your time comes to die, be not like those
> whose hearts are filled with fear of death,
> so that when their time comes they weep and pray
> for a little more time to live their lives over again
> in a different way. No.
> Sing your death song, and die like a hero going home.'

Harry paused. 'Mike, have a good one.'

\* \* \* \* \*

### Sunday 19 October 1958

The thousands of British fans making their way to Casablanca were sure that, for the first time, a British driver would become World Champion. The forthcoming battle had been portrayed to them in newspapers and magazines as a classic confrontation between the dedicated 'coming professional' Stirling Moss and the cavalier, fun loving amateur Mike Hawthorn. It seemed that the whole of Fleet Street was out in force, the popular press ready to create as much drama as they could while the 'superior' motoring press aimed to cover every aspect of the race in technical detail for the true enthusiasts.

The circuit was situated in desolate landscape south of Casablanca, but the great white city had been deserted since early morning by men seemingly stepping out of pictures from the Bible. They jostled with women who were clad with all the elegance of the Parisian fashion salons, the colour and variety of their costume helping to create the atmosphere of a screen epic. Adding to the scene were parading troops from the Moroccan army, smart and picturesque in their white tunics, baggy pantaloons, gaiters and boots, some turbaned, others proudly wearing their red tarboosh head-dress.

The photographers were keen to capture the scene with a backdrop of spray from the white Atlantic breakers glistening like diamonds in the misty sunlight.

All this prompted Basil Cardew to jot down that Monaco had at last been 'upstaged as the most colourful and romantic of settings'.

However, for the drivers stepping into their cars on the baking hot grid, it was far from glamorous. Not only was it unbearably hot but they faced racing on public roads that were, as yet, unused to competition. In this alone it was a prospect more dangerous than Reims or the Nürburgring. In practice most of the drivers had discovered places around the circuit where to stay on the pace would test their courage. Mike, with the need to stay energised in the heat and humidity, had reason to be the most fearful.

Averages based on statistics suggested that there would be at least one accident endangering life during the race. It was particularly concerning for the drivers and their wives and girlfriends that circuit owners, as well as the FIA, had made no progress, or even effort, to improve safety standards, neither on the track, nor inside the car. At the end of a season that had seen the deaths of two Grand Prix drivers and a number of injuries, the survivors still spurned safety belts, still preferring to be ejected from the cockpit. The winner of the race was likely to be someone whose concern for his own safety was evenly balanced by his readiness to drive for periods on the outer ribbon of the ragged edge, with all the risk that it entailed. It was all a question of money. Without the commercialisation of the sport an improvement in safety standards would be a long time coming.

Mike, sitting on pole position, glanced sideways at Stirling sitting alongside him, seemingly relaxed and staring calmly ahead. Was it not better to be here with all his senses on fire than sitting at home paralysed by the fear of dying?

'Sing your death song, and die like a hero going home.' The last line spoken by Harry came back as he had spoken it, in that slow Texan drawl.

In the practice sessions Mike's nervousness had succeeded in eliminating morbid thoughts. He was living in the 'here and now' rather than feeling pity for himself at home. He could actually look forward to something, the moment when he would cross the finish line in supreme joy as world champion, an experience that he would try to keep at the forefront of his consciousness. What was the phrase from the gravestone?

'One glorious hour?' Or was it 'one crowded hour?' At that moment he no longer felt guilt over Pete's death because he thought him lucky. At least he had gone quickly, without pain.

He looked past Stirling at Stuart, sitting next to him. Stuart saw him looking and gave him a big grin. Mike mouthed 'thanks' while shaking his raised thumb rapidly in tribute. It brought a big smile to Stuart's face and he reciprocated the gesture.

Stirling, although aware of movement around him, nevertheless remained still and composed, a picture of concentration. Mike settled back, made his last minute checks, took a last drink from his water bottle then handed it to his attendant mechanic...

The stage was set. The protagonists were in place. The warm-up lap was complete.

The flag was raised – and then it fell.

Stirling was instantly out of the blocks and shot immediately into the lead.

In those few seconds Tavoni's plan, hatched with Mike, to beat Stirling was all but scotched. Tavoni had ordered Phil Hill, in an unwitting carbon copy of

Pete Collins's own initiative at Silverstone, to force Stirling to chase him in the hope that he would blow up his engine in the process. But it was a case of Phil chasing Stirling. Would he get past and take up his prescribed role as the hot pacemaker? The reality was that Phil managed to chase Stirling for the first two laps, but was so eager to draw level that he overcooked it in a braking zone and careered into an escape road.

Now, with Phil seemingly out of the race, Mike's job was simple. All he needed to do was remain in second place to be crowned world champion. By the end of lap 11 over a fifth of the race had been completed and he still lay second, his hopes rising by the minute. He was further buoyed up by the surprising sight of Phil Hill's Ferrari in his mirror. Somehow, Phil had got back into the race and had hauled himself past driver after driver, determined to help Mike all he could. His amazing effort was rewarded when, on lap 18, he overtook Mike without a customary wave, so intent was he in trying to claw back Stirling's lead.

It was at this point that, ominously, Mike felt a sudden loss of energy accompanied by a sharper pain replacing the dull ache in his back. Mike automatically began to slow down, his lack of pace confirmed when he saw the 'hurry up' signal from his pits.

On lap 20 he saw Tony Brooks coming up in his mirrors, and on the same lap, passing him. At the same time Stirling was steadily increasing his lead over Phil Hill at the rate of one second per lap. Mike realised that it would need to be the drive of his life to rescue the situation. Without it he would have to rely on Stirling's car breaking down.

'Fuck it!'

It was more of an expletive aimed at the malevolent fates than the two Vanwalls ahead. But feeling anger was an efficient way of injecting more adrenalin into his nervous system. He kept telling himself to keep feeling that anger. If he should die in the attempt by either collapsing at the wheel or crashing at a corner, what did it matter? Was it not a case of 'better to lose and die' than 'win and die later?'

No, it was not. The latter was preferable but the former was okay by him.

Mike, with approximately one hour of the race left, began to drive not as if his life depended on it, but because it did not. The bolts of adrenalin produced by risky manoeuvres gave him more energy. His senses were back at their sharpest. He could now revert back to hitting each braking point on target, corner by corner and lap by lap, while taking up the racing line with perfectly timed gear changes.

There was another advantage that he had over his fellow competitors. One of the symptoms of kidney failure is a feeling of coldness and that handicap suddenly and miraculously came to his aid. While other drivers were suffering from the oppressive heat he felt normal, enabling him to keep up his concentration. He played games with himself, pretending that the race commentator was forecasting Stirling would win the championship. It helped keep the adrenalin pump working.

On lap 30 Mike's massive effort was rewarded as he hauled back Tony Brooks to within two seconds. The crowd were on their feet applauding his charge. The commentator's excited voice boomed around the circuit announcing that the race for the world title had been resumed.

Mike's blood red Ferrari began snapping at the heels of the green Vanwall, first on the back of the circuit along the Boulevard Panoramique, then at the Alexandra 90 degree corner into the Azenmour road. Tony Brooks did all he could, utilising his car's superior cornering ability to make it difficult for Mike to overtake.

As both drivers braked for the right hander into the finish straight Tony, under pressure from Mike, dropped into a lower gear than intended, shooting his rev counter needle into the red zone. There was an instantaneous explosion depositing oil on the track so quickly that the rear wheels of his car slid on it, whip lashing it towards a low wall.

At the last moment the spinning car slowed down and stopped. He clambered out rapidly and jumped over the wall – just in time – as Olivier Gendebien's Ferrari also spun on the pool of oil and was rammed by the Cooper-Climax driven by Francoise Picard. A second slower in his escape and Tony would have been killed.

Mike was aware of the accident but was forced to take note of the lap board held out to him, urging him to overtake Phil whose lapboard instructed him to let Mike through into second place. Phil did so and as Mike drew level urged him on waving his arm enthusiastically. Should Mike remain in his championship winning position Stirling's achievement, giving himself an astounding one minute and 10 seconds lead, would prove useless.

At last Mike could find respite and drop off the pace. His adrenalin was running low and the pain in his back forced him to ram two painkillers down his throat while ordering himself to keep station. With only 14 minutes of the race left he kept repeating the mantra: 'Keep going…keep going…'

Suddenly ahead arose a huge pillar of black smoke. In a flash he knew what it meant and dreaded what he might see. As he approached the scene of the accident he slowed down in shock – warning flags being waved, a raging fire on the inside of the track within a dense curtain of oily smoke, track marshals scurrying about. Then out of the inferno stumbled a man on fire, small and slim and wearing a body belt. Mike watched in horror as Stuart approached him, arms stretched out beseeching help.

He caught a glimpse of him falling to the ground and only then was he plastered with foam from a number of fire extinguishers.

The race was not stopped and Mike drove on. All thoughts of the world championship, the 'crowded' or 'glorious' hour, as he followed Stirling towards the finish line, were rendered meaningless. Tears ran underneath his visor. He cried for the eager to please, the gentle generous man.

He saw the chequered flag waved at him as he crossed the finish line and then ran into the pits, coming to a standstill, his body sagging over the wheel. Someone removed his helmet. He felt cold water poured over his head. He heard someone say 'Olivier's got broken ribs and Francois's got a terrible head injury.'

'Mike, you okay?'

He was extricated from the car and helped into the garage and sat down in a fog of exhaustion, confusion and misery. Eventually he was led out on to the track where the table stood bearing the world championship trophy. A large wreath of laurels was placed around his neck. He faced the battery of photographers as somehow he managed to shake hands with the prize donor. He held the world championship trophy and his mouth cracked open into a grin for more photography.

'No,' said Duncan. 'He's not giving interviews.' Then he was surrounded by drivers with their congratulations. And he was crying.

Stirling was one of the well wishers who came to him.

'You did it, you old so and so!' he exclaimed. 'Fantastic Mike.'

Tavoni now embraced him. 'We'll do it again next year!'

Mike found it difficult to breathe.

'I have your contract, Mike in the hotel. It's open. You name your money. Enzo gives you the world because you won the world.'

'No Tav. I've done. I've retired,' he managed to gasp.

There were thousands of British fans disappointed not to see the Golden Boy tour the circuit and hail them on what should have been a World Championship lap. The young man from Reims and whose glass of beer was spilt in the later race had waited patiently, determined that his hero would take it from him this time.

Stirling had already completed his victory lap and everyone in the crowd had applauded his tremendous drive. But the question ran through the masses, where was Mike? The same question was being asked after the ceremony. Normally there would be a celebration in the paddock when team owners, independent drivers, families and friends would come to enthuse and congratulate the world champion. And there was the prize for the top scoring Constructor of the year. It was won by Vanwall. Tony Vandervell received congratulations for that and commiserations for Stirling's failure. It was the converse in Tavoni's case, commiserations for being runner-up in the Constructors Championship and congratulations for Mike's achievement. In between all of this he had to keep explaining to enquirers that Mike was exhausted and needed to rest.

When the crowd had vanished from the circuit Duncan took him back to the hotel where he lay in the bath for a while. Later, he slept for four hours.

Duncan came to his room at 7.30pm and told him that Harry, Roy Salvadori, Graham Hill and Cliff Allison wanted to take him to The Casablanca, a night club within a few minutes walking distance. It was better, Duncan thought, that he spent the evening with friends. After all, he was now World Champion and a photograph or two would be expected of him celebrating.

Taking in Mike's misery, he deeply sympathised and asked if he would rather stay behind, after all. Mike slowly pushed himself upright and got out of bed. Before he left the hotel he sent a cable to Louise who was playing in *Romanoff and Juliet* at The National Theatre in Washington.

'We have done it mon ami matess. Will write soon. Love mon ami mate. Michael.'

During the evening Harry spoke with Tony Vandervell who had accompanied Stuart to Casablanca Hospital. He was told that he was alive and fighting hard. The next day he would be stretchered aboard the Vanwall chartered aircraft back to Heathrow, from where he would be taken by ambulance to the Burns Unit at East Grinstead Hospital. A nurse would accompany him on the flight.

Mike had just been given this news when a tipsy customer teetered towards him with a glass of wine and raised it to him. 'Here's looking at you, kid,' he said.

\* \* \* \* \*

Back home, they went to see Stuart in hospital and stood at his bedside looking at the motionless, white shrouded figure with the moving eyes. Tony Vandervell, who loved the little man, was the first to break away in tears, cursing his 'stupid hobby' of building racing cars. Mike remained at the bedside with Harry and Tony Brooks, no one capable of speech. Walking down the corridor they had passed photographs of British fighter pilots who had raised funds for the unit, the place where Sir Archibald McIndoe had pioneered plastic surgery and for which many were truly grateful. As Stuart's eyes remained on him Mike felt humbled and diminished by the little man's fighting spirit.

\* \* \* \* \*

**Mayfair Hotel London, 24 October 1958**

Mike was the star guest at the annual British Racing Drivers' Club dinner dance. There he was presented with the Club's Gold Star award. He made a speech in which he hoped that the Board of Trade would prevail upon the Society of Motor manufacturers to allow a Vanwall to be displayed at the Motor Show. This little act of patriotism was to make up for him winning the championship in a foreign make of car. He had intended to announce his retirement at the dinner but had not wanted to spoil the evening and so kept it for another day. Winifred, at last, could understand his motive and had approved.

Stirling Moss then made a speech congratulating Mike who was photographed standing at the side of the stage giving him 'the two fingers'.

Mike was reading a newspaper at breakfast the next morning when he caught sight of his photograph taken at the dinner. He was stricken at the sight of his bloated face. He looked more like 49, he thought, than 29. He tried to keep it away from his mother but she insisted on being handed the newspaper. On seeing his photograph she was, as he had anticipated, shocked by what she saw.

'Oh Mike,' she said pained. 'Look at you.'

But then she changed her tone when sack loads of invitations and tempters began to arrive at the house, including lucrative endorsements of commercial products. 'Think of the money you're going to make, you'll be made for life. Especially selling Ferraris. Now tell me, Mike, for God's sake, when are you going to tell everybody you've retired?'

The telephone rang and Mike went to answer it. He came back shortly to sit down heavily.

After a pause he said, 'Stuart's died.' Another pause. 'Thank God.'

# **Chapter** Fifteen

On 29 October Mike attended Stuart's funeral with Duncan. Tony Brooks and Tony Vandervell joined them. Having suffered during the funerals of Luigi and Pete he came in hope, feeling that he had grieved enough. However, he was totally unprepared for a different kind of remorse.

He had never treated Pete as he had Stuart, with a tolerance based on latent contempt. He had used him for his own benefit. Having taken all that he needed he had given nothing back. The image of the helpless, burning and pleading figure came back to haunt him as soon as the coffin appeared in church. At the pronouncement: 'I am the resurrection and the life' he was gone, his body bent and wracked with an emotion that was greater, if anything, than he had felt at Pete's funeral.

After the service he sat with Duncan in his car, rain streaming down its windows, waiting to follow the family cars on their journey to the crematorium. He stared straight ahead, taking in short spasmodic breaths as words formed on his open lips and then vanished.

Duncan, about to turn the key in the ignition, glanced at him, winced a little, then put out a hand to clasp his shoulder. Mike turned to him with a smile and nodding his head, crumbled into yet more tears.

\* \* \* \* \*

In the weeks since he won the championship Mike had been faced with the impossible task of dealing with the mass of letters that flooded into the house each day. At first Winifred would have nothing to do with it, claiming that to get excited over them would only serve to tempt him back into motor racing. And when, for the umpteenth time of asking, would he announce his retirement?

The pile of propositions from companies anxious to give Mike money grew rapidly. In post-war austerity Britain this kind of proposition, even on a small scale, was very limited. From being a detractor of motor racing Winifred metamorphosed into an outright enthusiast. This was fortunate for Mike, who saw no future for himself and regarded every material thing as useless, and so was content to allow her to recruit a friend to help her wade through the post.

At times he would think about Pete and Stuart – even Luigi – and think how lucky they were to be already dead. He was not yet on morphine and so only had the consultant's assurance that there would be no pain at the end. One thing puzzled him, Winifred's apparent blindness to his state of health. He failed to realise that her myopic view of his illness had begun after the death of Pete Collins when she had started, deep down, to build up a defence mechanism against what should have become obvious, that Mike's illness was more serious than she imagined. Now, with all the attendant publicity in becoming world champion, it precluded any such doubts in her mind. How could he have won the championship without being fit?

On 1 November Mike attended the last day of the Earls Court Motor Show in London. As a UK concessionary agent for the sale of Ferrari sports cars he stood on Stand 118, smartly dressed in a dark suit and tie, positioned between two right-hand drive Ferrari 250 GT cars. The camera captured him with one arm straight down at his side while the palm and fingers of the other were sunk in the side pocket of his jacket, with the thumb resting on the top edge, the ideal pose, the Public Relations Officer had advised him, 'one that the Duke of Edinburgh adopted'. In short, it created a sense of dignity matched with sociability. The PRO would have been disturbed had the cameras been able to reveal the inside of Mike's pocket, where his fingers clutched a pill box containing morphine tablets.

On Tuesday 11 November Mike attended Buckingham Palace, one of seven invited guests, all of them outstanding sportsmen in their field. The Queen spoke to him and asked about his future. Would he still be driving for Ferrari the following year? Mike lied, saying that he hoped it would be the case.

A week later on Wednesday 19 November the big grin was once more on display, this time in his home town of Farnham where a dinner was held in his honour at the Bush Hotel. The chairman of the Council expressed his admiration for the 'courage, concentration and will power' that he had shown.

On 5 December he attended a function held by the British Racing Drivers' Club. By this time the request for endorsements had ceased and it was time, Winifred said, that he should declare his retirement and Mike agreed to do so at the dinner.

However, the *Daily Express* stymied him by announcing that it was ending its association with the Club and marked the occasion by presenting the club chairman with a cheque for £10,000 as a mark of its gratitude. It caused expressions of regret and dismay when announced and Mike was forced to think desperately hard. If he announced that 'The Golden Boy' was also retiring from the sport after becoming world champion only eight weeks previously, it would prove a double blow for the BRDC. Out of consideration for the feelings of its members he waited until the next day when he rang Alan Brinton of *The News Chronicle* who went along to see him at the TT Garage.

Mike was running a duster over his beloved Jaguar 3.4 saloon as he arrived.

'I've been thinking of retiring for some time,' he said.

'Have you told Enzo Ferrari yet Mike?'

'Yes. I've written to him. It's better to go out at the top.'

'Was it Pete Collins who made you decide?'

Mike thought about it. Then it suddenly struck him that Pete had not featured in his thoughts since Casablanca, when before that date he had been dominant. Even in the moment of his great victory he had felt no relief in having paid off his debt.

In reply to the question he told Brinton that Pete had been his inspiration and he had won the Championship as much for him, as for himself. And would Alan be sure to report that?

Later that night, when fear of dying was strong and his philosophical notes on death and its meaning were of little help, he found himself thinking morbid thoughts and scenes at Luigi's funeral flashed into his mind, causing him to sweat and switch on the light. Although it was late he suddenly rang Duncan and asked if he would mind driving him to Stone Church in Staffordshire the following morning.

Duncan said he would, willingly, but pointed out that it might snow. He did, however, reassure Mike that he had the latest and best heater fitted to his car – at a time when only a few cars had them as a factory fitting – and so promised the consolation of a comfortable journey.

They arrived at the church when snow was falling and darkness descending. The latest weather forecast en route had not promised any relief from the wintry conditions.

'We're not going to get back in this,' Duncan said. 'The roads are going to be bloody awful. There's a pub we passed down the road. I think it's got rooms. I'll nip back while you do your thing.'

Mike reached into the back seats of the car and drew out his world championship laurel wreath and entered the churchyard to the sound of the car starting up and driving away.

He stood at Pete's graveside a moment in contemplation and then bent down to stand the heavy wreath against the headstone so that the carved name 'Peter Collins' featured in the open centre. A printed label was attached to the wreath which read:'Champion of the world'. Snow flakes began to adorn the wreath as he stood upright and gave a nod. 'You did it mate,' he said. 'You did it.' He remained in contemplation for a moment and then broke away.

They spent the night in Stone and were lucky to find a rapid thaw setting in the following morning. On arriving home Mike contacted his solicitor with a view to adding to his will an annual settlement for his illegitimate son in France. There was an additional amendment to make. In his first will, written in 1956, he had left everything to his mother, but now he decided that Duncan should take custody of his trophies and considerable memorabilia as he was uncertain as to how Winifred might regard them after his death.

On Christmas Day the pain was too severe and he stayed in bed. Without realising, his body had come to tolerate the analgesic effects of morphine. Thus he was forced to take more than the prescribed dose. This had produced drowsiness. His skin became clammy and his breathing shallow. Winifred, shocked by what she saw, called the doctor who found that his pulse rate had dropped alarmingly.

'Hasn't he told you?' said the doctor when they went downstairs.

'Told me what?'

The doctor paused and asked her to sit down.

'Is he very ill?' Winifred put a hand to her chest. 'Is he...'

'I'm sorry, but he hasn't got long to live.'

She blinked a little and hesitantly touched the side of her face. 'I think I knew...I never asked...never...' Her voice tailed away and she remained silent.

After a few minutes the doctor went back upstairs to see Mike and take away his morphine tablets, telling him that he was giving him 'a more suitable narcotic, for the time being'.

On New Year's Eve Mike felt well enough to eat downstairs, even managed to show humour when Winifred read out to him an announcement of the New Year's Honours awards by the Queen. One such recipient was Stirling Moss.

'Mike, he's been given the OBE,' she said.

'What's that?' said Mike, 'Order of the Bald 'ead?'

Winifred stared at him in astonishment and began to laugh.

'Mike, that is the funniest thing!'

Her laughter soon changed to weeping, at which Mike stood up to give her a big, comforting hug.

On 10 January the doctor paid Mike his second visit that week. After examining him, he returned his morphine tablets with strict instructions as to their use. Mike was happy and relieved to see them again. Winifred noted that the depression that had lain over him like a grey blanket, now seemed to have lifted. It seemed that he had given himself up to enjoying the time he had left.

\* \* \* \* \*

On Wednesday 21 January Louise called Mike after completing her highly successful tour of the States with *Romanoff and Juliet*, saying that she had arrived in England and was staying at The Westbury Hotel in Mayfair. She had not been able to speak to him before his victory, and had only sent a congratulatory cable.

'Mike, sweetheart, loads of congratulations,' she said. 'Pete said you'd do it. How are you, are you okay?' Her voice was loaded with warmth and sympathy.

To Mike it sounded sexy, even though sex was the last thing on his mind.

'Yeah, I'm fine. I miss you.' He could not help sounding intimate. Whatever happened, Mike knew that it would probably be their last meeting at which he would confess everything about his guilt and remorse over Pete's death. He needed her absolution to make his restoration final and complete. But would he tell her he was dying? It was impossible to decide. Meeting her would be highly emotional, of that he was certain. They arranged that he would drive up to London the next day and they would take tea at Fortnum and Masons in Piccadilly. He had one or two things to do in town beforehand, but assured her he would be on time.

Mike woke up the following morning, feeling tired as usual. He drove to the TT Garage, arriving at 9.30am, remembering that he had to leave on time in order to meet Billy Butlin, the holiday camp tycoon, at the Cumberland Hotel, Marble Arch, where he was to judge a charity 'motor scooter' contest. After that he would meet Louise. Following that he would drive home to meet Duncan, who would then take him to the Garage where, in front of witnesses, he would sign the document cementing their car sales and garage partnership. After discharging that duty he intended to return home to rest until it was time for him to be taken by Duncan to be Guest of

Honour at the annual dinner of the Farnham and District section of the Motor Agents Association. There, Duncan and others would sing his praises in what promised to be a jolly affair.

However, his intentions that day were upset when a greater tiredness enveloped him on arrival at the Garage that morning. To the employees he looked paler than usual and one had even seen him sitting on a step with his head in his hands for at least 10 minutes. When asked if he was alright he said he had a bit of a headache but would take an aspirin for it.

An hour later he appeared to recover enough to go to his car saying that he was 'off up to town' and would be back by late afternoon.

He sat in the car and paused a moment, as he always did, to smell the leather – except that this time it was not as strong as usual. He closed his eyes and then opened them again with a grimace. He was bloody knackered wasn't he? There was no way in which he could drive to London and back. The pity he felt at not seeing Louise caused him to suddenly switch on the ignition, but after a pause, switch it off. He was being bloody stupid. He decided to go home from where he would ring Louise and seek her blessing. He would talk with her for as long as it took. He would then ring Duncan, asking if he could pay him the visit at lunchtime, much earlier than arranged.

Satisfied that he had covered all eventualities, he fired the engine of his Jaguar and was about to drive off when a grey, gull-winged Mercedes 300SL drove slowly past the garage. The driver was Rob Walker, a friend. Seeing Mike he pressed a button and his car door winged sideways into the air allowing him to deliver an outstretched teasing two-fingered salute. The door then closed and the Mercedes drew away, taking the right-hand fork towards Guildford.

Mike, regardless of his condition, felt a bolt of energy flood through his body, stung by the challenge from a 'Kraut' car – his Jaguar costing a third of the price of the German made Mercedes. He picked up the gauntlet and followed. Rob saw him in his mirror and slowed sufficiently for Mike to draw closer until he could see his number plate, ROB 1. The race was on. At over 100 miles per hour the two cars sped towards Guildford along The Hog's Back, a stretched out and fiercely windswept hilltop. Coming down off the ridge the road became a dual carriageway that appeared deserted.

Neck and neck they went, Rob and Mike grinning at each other. Mike took the Mercedes before a right-hand bend, passing it flat out.

The Jaguar's tail twitched, but instead of slowing down, he pressed on even harder, causing the tail to slide out further. It struck the roadside kerb. Spinning right around, for a moment the two drivers faced each other, Mike and his opponent. But instead of backing off Mike kept his foot down – and was there a smile?

The car continued backwards, struck a bollard and headed for a lorry coming from the opposite direction. Clipping its tail it disappeared into a cloud of mud and water before striking a tree in the hedgerow. The car was virtually split in two on impact.

Rob Walker stopped his car and ran across to find Mike lying full length in the back seat, just in time to see his eyes glaze over and face and body become still.

The manager of Coombs Garage, situated near to the accident, was quickly on the scene. He knew Mike well. Then a family doctor, who had stopped for petrol at the garage, followed and pronounced death. There was some initial confusion as to the ownership of the Jaguar, it resembling one owned by Duncan, neither car possessing a personal number plate. In consequence someone rang him. Shocked by the news, he asked about Mike. Were they positive it was him? There was no doubt, he was told.

The news spread quickly. Some time later Duncan remembered Louise, knew that she was due to meet Mike that afternoon. In desperation he rang the Westbury Hotel, needing to prevent her from getting the news from a stranger. He did not know that newspaper placards were, at that very moment, being prepared for display on the streets of London.

'MIKE HAWTHORN DEAD'

In fact Louise was walking into the Westbury Hotel as he talked to the hotel receptionist. She was spotted by one of the desk staff who happened to be a motor racing fan. He was about to ask if she had heard the news when the receptionist came to the desk telling Louise that he had a 'gentleman on the line'. Would she like to take the call at the desk or in her room?

'Who is it?' she said.

'Mr Duncan Hamilton.'

Louise, sickly afraid, went to her room where she spoke hesitantly to Duncan and had her worst fears confirmed.

'Maybe it was for the best,' he said.

There was a long pause before Louise spoke. 'Duncan,' she said slowly, 'I knew he was ill but are you telling me…he was dying?'

'Yes.'

'You mean his kidney problem? I knew about that but…'

'Yes. It was.' Duncan was relieved that she knew. 'He tried to hide it.'

'Yes.'

After the call Louise lay on the bed for a few minutes, but then summoned up enough composure to ring for a taxi to take her to whichever station ran trains to Guildford.

Meanwhile, Duncan had remembered his promise to Mike that should he die in an accident he would be identified by him, not by his mother. Thoughts of Winifred caused him to rush out of the house and drive over to see her before the press got to her doorstep.

On arrival there were a couple of photographers and a local reporter already outside the house, but kept back by an off duty policeman who took it upon himself to protect her privacy. Knowing that she had been told of Mike's death gave Duncan time to calm himself before ringing the doorbell.

He found her strangely quiet, seemingly placid, with no sign of undue shock. He talked gently about the need for identification and that he would perform that task, but did she want to accompany him?

They arrived at Guildford Hospital mortuary and she remained in the car while Duncan went inside. Ten minutes later he emerged and came back to the car.

'He didn't suffer,' he said. 'There's not a mark on him.'

When he had delivered her back to the house she made tea while declaring that she wanted no one from motor racing to contact her – if Duncan could possibly speak to those who might want to? He promised to do his best.

It was while he was inside the house that Louise arrived by taxi, having caught a train from London. She was told by the policeman that Duncan was inside with Mrs Hawthorn. The reporter sniffed a story and asked her if she would not mind telling him who she was.

At that moment Duncan left the house.

'Louise.' He said, surprised.

'Hallo Duncan. I caught a train. I had to come.'

She went back to the taxi, paid the driver and took out the bunch of flowers she had bought outside the railway station, and pinned to it a note she had written. Could Duncan take her to visit the place where it happened?

The late January afternoon was getting dark when they arrived at the accident site on the A3. A squall lashed the windscreen, forcing them to remain inside the car for a few minutes. Duncan took a torch from the glove box. As the rain began to thin out, they stepped out of the car and looked around. The wreck of the Jaguar had been taken away. Curiously, there was already a bunch of flowers placed alongside the hedgerow, but with no accompanying note.

Louise took out the telegram that Mike had sent her with the news that he had become world champion. She read it aloud, shining the torch.

'We have done it mon ami matess.' She stressed the 'we' and looked at Duncan.

'He meant Pete, didn't he,' she said.

Duncan thought that her guess was probably correct and later told her the full story.

\* \* \* \* \*

Enzo Ferrari – whose anger at Mike informing him that he had retired had now abated on hearing the grim news – stood in the shrine room and lit a candle, placing it in front of a photograph of Mike standing adjacent to that of Pete. He then went to the doorway and spoke to the well-dressed woman sitting in an armchair and smoking a cigarette.

'Carlotta?'

She put down the cigarette in an ash tray and joined him to stand before the shrine. Together they said a short prayer for the dead. A tear fell down her cheek. Enzo's eyes too, began to water. Afterwards, he asked her if it was true that she had placed a curse on Mike and Pete.

She denied it.

\* \* \* \* \*

On 28 January 1959 Mike Hawthorn's funeral took place at St Andrews, the local parish church. It was packed with mourners. Hundreds more stood outside. Winifred had wanted it to be private, putting 'Michael', the mother's son, to rest and not 'Mike' the public's Golden Boy. But the media interest was intense with journalists and reporters from the world over intent on recording the occasion.

Louise, Duncan and Stirling were present, the latter by now having a commercial manager, marking his 'professionalism' as a racing driver.

Asked by Basil Cardew if he had thought of quitting the sport following so many tragedies he replied, 'No, not a bit of it.'

Afterwards the coffin was taken to West Street Cemetery in Farnham. There, crowds lined the streets, with men doffing their hats in respect. Louise and Duncan joined the many who were already surveying the rows of floral tributes and wreaths, laid out in their hundreds. 'Oh no,' she said suddenly and picked up a small wreath. It had a card attached that read:

'A mon papa. Michael.'

Looking furtively around she opened her coat and hid the wreath before Winifred, who was escorted by family friends, could come across it.

\* \* \* \* \*

A memorial service was held for Mike on 6 February 1959 at St Columba's Church, Knightsbridge, London. Winifred felt that she could not bear to listen to the eulogies about her son and so stayed away. It was Louise who was prominent, called upon to read out lines from the poet Thomas Mordaunt.

'Sound, sound the clarion, fill the fife,
Throughout the sensual world proclaim
One crowded hour of glorious life
is worth an age without a name.'

She ended with:

'True love is true friendship. It can mean self sacrifice. Mike was the world motor racing champion but as a true, loving friend, one who would repay any debt, he was an even greater champion.'

## End Notes

• Taffy Von Trips died two years later in an accident at Monza.

• Harry Schell died the following year racing at Silverstone.

• Stirling Moss never won the World Drivers' Championship.

• Louise went back to America and continued with her career.